John Barrow

MUTINY ON THE BOUNTY

Published in this edition 1997 by Peter Haddock Ltd,
Pinfold Lane, Bridlington, East Yorkshire YO16 5BT

Illustrated by John Marshall

ISBN 0 7105 1016 0

Printed and bound in France
by Maury Eurolivres

10 9 8 7 6 5 4 3 2 1

Contents

To the Reader

When you have seen and enjoyed a film or TV programme that has been made from a famous book, you may decide to read the book.

Then what happens? You get the book and, it's more than likely, you get a shock as well! You turn ten or twenty pages, and nothing seems to *happen*. Where are all the lively people and exciting incidents? When, you say, will the author get down to telling the story? In the end you will probably throw the book aside and give it up. Now, why is that?

Well, perhaps the author was writing for adults and not for children. Perhaps the book was written a long time ago, when people had more time for reading and liked nothing better than a book that would keep them entertained for weeks.

We think differently today. That's why some of these wonderful books have been retold for you. If you enjoy them in this shorter form, then when you are older you will go back to the original books and enjoy all the more the stories they have to tell.

About the Author

John Barrow was born in Ulverston in 1764 and worked as a timekeeper in an iron foundry in Liverpool, as a whaler in Greenland and as a teacher of mathematics in London before accompanying Lord Macartney to China and South Africa, where he proved to be an extremely able administrator.

In 1804 he was appointed secretary to the Admiralty, a post that he held for most of the next forty years and in which he did much to encourage expeditions to the Arctic, including those by Sir John Ross, Sir James Clark Ross and Sir John Franklin. In 1830 he was one of the founders of what became the Royal Geographical Society. Point Barrow and the Barrow Straits in the Arctic and Cape Barrow in Antarctica are named after him.

His account of the mutiny of the crew of the *Bounty* was published in 1831. He was knighted in 1835 and died in 1848.

Chapter One

Island Paradise – Tahiti and the Breadfruit

The South Pacific islands of Tahiti made a great impression upon the imagination of British sailors of the eighteenth century. King George III was on the throne in London. He was keenly interested in geography and the development of scientific knowledge, and gave his support to numerous scientific expeditions to the Pacific region, so far away from Britain and the chilly north. The sailors, both officers and men, fell quickly under the charm of the islands and the islanders. The climate was warm and sunny, and abundant food grew on wild trees and bushes. The people, though apprehensive and hostile at first, soon showed they were friendly, peaceable and easy-going. Even at the best of times, a sailor's existence was hard and dangerous. Compared to life on even the best-run British man-of-war, Tahiti seemed an earthly paradise.

One of the British visitors was Captain Cook, on his first voyage to the Pacific, in 1769. There were some drawbacks to be noted in the island paradise. The Otaheitans, as the Tahitians were then called, could not resist pilfering. "I must bear my testimony," wrote Captain Cook, "that the people of this country, of all ranks, men and women, are the arrantest thieves upon the face of the earth."

Despite this predilection to stealing, the British visitors found the islanders attractive and welcoming. The Otaheitans were graceful people, and their behaviour to strangers and to each other was affable and courteous. In their character, they appeared to be brave, open and candid, without suspicion or treachery, cruelty or revenge.

The greater part of the food of Otaheitans was vegetable. Pigs, dogs and poultry were their only animals, and all of these were eaten as food. "We all agreed," says Cook, "that a South-Sea dog was little inferior to an English lamb," which he ascribed to its being fed wholly on vegetables. The cook first killed the dog by holding his hands close over his mouth and nose for the space of a quarter of an hour. A hole was then made in the ground, about a foot deep, in which a fire was kindled and some small stones placed in layers, alternately with the wood, to be heated. The dog was then singed, scraped with a shell, and the hair taken off as clean as if it had been scalded in hot water. It was then cut up with the same instrument and the entrails carefully washed. When the

hole was sufficiently heated, the fire was taken out, and some of the stones, being placed at the bottom, were covered with green leaves. The dog, with the entrails, was then placed on the leaves and, other leaves laid on top, the whole was covered with the rest of the hot stones, and the mouth of the hole close-stopped with mould. In somewhat less than four hours, it was again opened and the dog taken out, excellently baked, and the party all agreed that it made a very good dish.

The vegetable food of the Otaheitans consisted of various preparations of breadfruit, coconuts, bananas, plantains and a great variety of other fruit, the spontaneous products of a rich soil and genial climate. Breadfruit, when baked in the same way as the dog, became soft and not unlike a boiled potato. Much of this fruit was gathered before it was ripe and then underwent the two states of fermentation – the saccharine and acetous, in the latter of which it was moulded into balls and called *mahie*. The Otaheitans seldom made a meal without this sour paste. Salt water was the universal sauce, without which no meal was eaten. Their drink in general consisted of water or the juice of the coconut. There was, however, one plant from the root of which they extracted a juice of an intoxicating quality, called *ava*, but Captain Cook's party saw nothing of its effects, probably because the Otaheitans considered drunkenness as a disgrace.

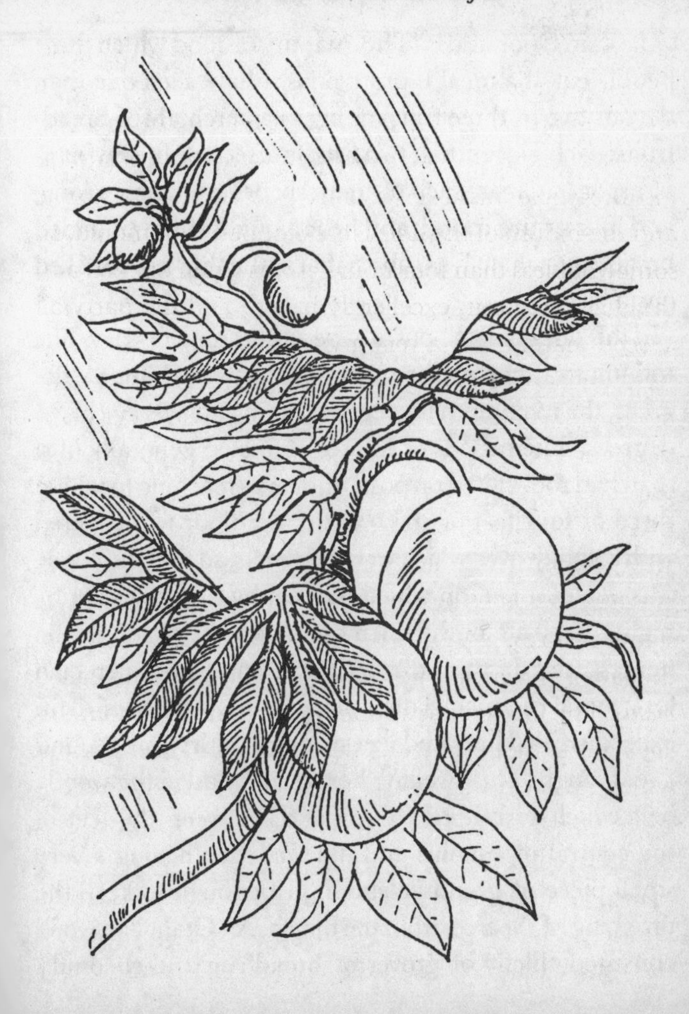

Captain Cook adds, "The quantity of food which these people eat at a meal is prodigious. I have seen one man devour two or three fishes as big as a perch; three bread-fruits, each bigger than two fists; fourteen or fifteen plantains, or bananas, each of them six or seven inches long, and four or five round; and near a quart of the pounded breadfruit, which is as substantial as the thickest unbaked custard."

In this fine climate houses were almost unnecessary. The minimum range of the thermometer was about 63 degrees, the maximum 85 degrees, giving an average of 74 degrees. Their sheds or houses consisted generally of a thatched roof raised on posts, the eaves reaching to within three or four feet of the ground; the floor was covered with soft hay, over which were laid mats, so that the whole was one cushion, on which they sat by day and slept by night. They ate in the open air, under the shade of the nearest tree. In each district there was a house erected for general use, much larger than common, some of them exceeding two hundred feet in length, thirty broad, and twenty high. The dwelling houses all stood in the woody belt which surrounded the island, between the feet of the central mountains and the sea, each having a very small piece of ground cleared, just enough to keep the dropping of the trees from the thatch. An Otaheitan wood consisted chiefly of groves of breadfruit and coconuts,

without underwood and intersected in all directions by the paths that led from one house to another. "Nothing," says Cook, "can be more grateful than this shade, in so warm a climate, nor anything more beautiful than these walks."

With all the activity they were capable of displaying, and the sprightliness of their disposition, the islanders had a life of ease. The trees that produced their food mostly grow wild – the breadfruit, coconut, bananas of thirteen sorts, besides plantains; a fruit not unlike an apple, which, when ripe, was very pleasant; sweet potatoes, yams, and a species of arum; the pandanus, the jambu and the sugar cane; and various plants whose roots were edible. These, with many others, were produced with so little cultivation, that, as Cook, observed, the islanders seemed to be exempted from the first general curse that "man should eat his bread in the sweat of his brow."

Such was the state of this beautiful island and its interesting and fascinating people at the time when Captain Cook visited it.

CHAPTER TWO
The *Bounty* Sets Sail

By the year 1787, seventeen years after Cook's return from his first voyage, London merchants owned great estates in the West Indies, and they wanted to have the breadfruit plant taken there to feed their workers. The government agreed to send a ship to Tahiti to collect breadfruit plants; and a vessel for the purpose was bought and fitted at Deptford on the River Thames. The arrangements for storing the plants were designed, in a very clever way, by Sir Joseph Banks, the famous scientist, who had been on one of the first British expeditions to Tahiti. He named the ship the *Bounty*, and recommended Lieutenant Bligh, who had been with Captain Cook, to command her. Her weight was about two hundred and fifteen tons, and her crew consisted of one lieutenant, who was commanding officer, one master, three warrant officers, one surgeon, two master's mates, two midshipmen and thirty-four petty officers and seamen, making in all a total of forty-four; to which were added two gardeners to manage on the voyage the plants intended for the West Indies, and other plants that were to

be brought home for King George III's garden at Kew.

On the 23rd December 1787, the *Bounty* sailed from Spithead, and on the 26th she met a severe storm of wind from the east, which continued for several days, in the course of which the ship suffered greatly. It was only with great difficulty and risk that they were able to secure the boats from being washed away. Besides other damage done in this storm, a large quantity of bread was soaked and rendered useless.

This made it desirable to touch at Tenerife to put the ship to rights, where they arrived on the 5th January 1788, and, having refitted the ship and taken on provisions, they sailed again on the 10th. "I now," says Bligh, in the journal he kept of the voyage, "divided the people into three watches, and gave the charge of the third watch to Mr Fletcher Christian, one of the mates. I have always considered this a desirable regulation when circumstances will admit of it, and I am persuaded that unbroken rest not only contributes much towards the health of the ship's company, but enables them more readily to exert themselves in cases of sudden emergency."

Wishing to proceed to Otaheite without stopping and the storm having diminished their supply of provisions, Bligh decided to put all hands on an allowance of two-thirds the normal ration of bread. It was also decided that water for drinking should be passed through filter-

ing stones that had been procured at Tenerife. "I now," says Bligh, "made the ship's company acquainted with the object of the voyage, and gave assurances of the certainty of promotion to every one whose endeavours should merit it."

By his own account, the commander did everything to make his officers and men comfortable and happy. He was himself a thoroughbred sailor and used every possible means to preserve the health of his crew. Continued rain and a close atmosphere had covered everything in the ship with mildew. She was therefore aired below with fires, and frequently sprinkled with vinegar, and every interval of dry weather was taken advantage of to open all the hatchways and clean the ship, and to have all the crew's wet things washed and dried. With these precautions to secure health, they passed the hazy and sultry atmosphere of the low latitudes without a single complaint.

On Sunday, the 2nd of March, Lieutenant Bligh notes, "On this day I gave to Mr Fletcher Christian, whom I had before desired to take charge of the third watch, a written order to act as lieutenant."

Having reached as far as the latitude of 36 degrees south, on the 9th March, "the change of temperature," he records, "began now to be sensibly felt, there being a variation in the thermometer, since yesterday, of eight

degrees. That the people might not suffer by their own negligence, I gave orders for their light tropical clothing to be put by, and made them dress in a manner more suited to a cold climate. I had provided for this before I left England, by giving directions for such clothes to be purchased as would be found necessary. On this day, on a complaint of the master, I found it necessary to punish Matthew Quintal, one of the seamen, with two dozen lashes, for insolence and mutinous behaviour. Before this I had not had occasion to punish any person on board."

Soon after this they encountered tremendous weather off Cape Horn, storms with hail and sleet, which made it necessary to keep a constant fire burning night and day; and one of the watch always attended to drying the crew's wet clothes. This stormy weather continued for nine days. The ship began to require pumping every hour; the decks became so leaky that the commander was obliged to allot the great cabin to those who had wet berths to hang their hammocks in. Finding they were losing ground every day and that it was hopeless to persist in attempting a passage by this route, at this season of the year, it was decided not to attempt rounding Cape Horn but to bear away for the Cape of Good Hope. The helm was accordingly put a-weather, to the great joy of every person on board.

They arrived at the Cape on the 23rd of May, and re-

mained there thirty-eight days to refit the ship, replenish provisions and refresh the crew. They sailed again on the 1st July and anchored in Adventure Bay in Van Dieman's Land (Australia) on the 20th August. Here they remained, taking on wood and water, till the 4th September. On the evening of the 25th October they saw Otaheite; and the next day came to anchor in Matavai Bay, after a distance which the ship had run since leaving England of twenty-seven thousand and eighty-six miles.

Otoo, the chief of the district, on hearing of the arrival of the *Bounty*, sent a small pig and a young plantain tree, as a token of friendship. The ship was now plentifully supplied with provisions, every man on board having as much as he could consume. As soon as the ship was secured, Lieutenant Bligh went on shore with the chief, Poeeno, passing through a walk delightfully shaded with breadfruit trees, to the chief's house, where his wife and her sister were busily employed staining a piece of cloth red. "In the course of two or three days," says he, "an intimacy between the natives and the ship's company was become so general, that there was scarcely a man in the ship who had not already his *tayo* or friend."

Nelson, the gardener, and his assistant, being sent out to look for young plants, reported on their return that, according to appearances, the object of the voyage would

probably be accomplished with ease. The plants were plentiful, and there was no apparent objection on the part of the Otaheitans to their collecting as many as might be wanted.

Presents were now given to Otoo, the Chief of Matavai, who had changed his name to Tinah. He was told that, on account of the kindness of his people to Captain Cook and from a desire to serve him and his country, King George III had sent out those valuable presents to him, and "will you not, Tinah," said Bligh, "send something to King George in return?"

"Yes," he said, "I will send him anything I have," and then began to enumerate the different articles in his power, among which he mentioned the breadfruit. This was the exact point to which Bligh was endeavouring to lead him, and he was immediately told that the breadfruit trees were what King George would like very much, on which he promised that a great many should be put on board.

Hitherto no thefts had been committed, and Bligh was congratulating himself on the improvement of the Otaheitans in this respect, as the same facilities and the same temptations were open to them as before. The ship, as on former occasions, was constantly crowded with visitors. One day, however, the gudgeon of the rudder belonging to the large cutter was drawn out and stolen,

without being seen by the sailor who was stationed to take care of her. As a result of this and other petty thefts, mainly resulting from the negligence of the sailors, and worrying about the possible effect on relations with the chiefs, "I thought," says Bligh, "it would have a good effect to punish the boat-keeper in their presence, and accordingly I ordered him a dozen lashes. All who attended the punishment interceded very earnestly to get it mitigated: the women showed great sympathy, and that degree of feeling which characterises the amiable part of their sex."

The longer they remained on the island, the more they had occasion to be pleased with the conduct of the islanders, and the less bothered they were, either on board or when on shore, by the Otaheitans following them as they had at first. In every house they wished to enter, they always experienced a kind reception.

CHAPTER THREE
Signs of Dissent among the Crew

The behaviour of the Otaheitans on all occasions was worthy of praise. One morning, however, when the watch was relieved, the small cutter was found to be missing. The ship's company were immediately mustered, when it was discovered that three men were absent. They had taken with them eight sets of arms and ammunition, but what their plan was, or which way they had gone, no one on board seemed to know.

When information was given of the route they had taken, the master was dispatched to search for the cutter, and one of the chiefs went with him. Before they had got halfway, however, they met the boat with five Otaheitans, who were bringing her back to the ship. For this service they were handsomely rewarded.

The chiefs promised to use every possible means to detect and bring back the deserters, which, in a few days, some of the islanders had so far accomplished as to seize and bind them, but let them loose again on a promise

that they would return to their ship, which they did not exactly fulfil, but gave themselves up soon afterwards when a search was made for them.

A few days after this, a much more serious occurrence happened that gave to the commander great concern. The wind had blown fresh in the night, and at daylight it was discovered that the cable by which the ship rode at anchor had been cut near the water's edge in such a way that only one strand of the cable remained whole.

While they were securing the ship, Tinah came on board, and although there was no reason whatever to suppose otherwise than that he was perfectly innocent, nevertheless, says Bligh, "I spoke to him in a very peremptory manner, and insisted upon his discovering and bringing to me the offender. He promised to use his utmost endeavours to discover the guilty person. The next morning he and his wife came to me, and assured me that they had made the strictest inquiries without success. This was not at all satisfactory, and I behaved towards them with great coolness, at which they were much distressed; and the lady at length gave vent to her sorrow by tears. I could no longer keep up the appearance of mistrusting them, but I earnestly recommended to them, as they valued the King of England's friendship, that they would exert their utmost endeavours to find out the offenders, which they faithfully promised to do."

Here Bligh observes that it had since occurred to him that this attempt to cut the ship adrift was most probably the act of some of his own men. Their wish to remain at Otaheite might have been answered without danger if the *Bounty* had been driven on to the shore. At the time it happened, he says, he entertained not the least thought of this kind, nor did the possibility of it enter into his head, he having no suspicion that so general a wish or so strong an attachment to these islands could prevail among his people as to induce them to abandon every prospect of returning home to their native country.

The *Bounty* arrived on the 26th October 1788 and remained till the 4th April 1789. On the 31st March, the Commander says: "Today, all the plants were on board, being in seven hundred and seventy-four pots, thirty-nine tubs, and twenty-four boxes. While active preparations for departure were going on, the good chief Tinah, on bringing a present for King George, could not refrain from shedding tears. During the remainder of their stay, there appeared among the natives an evident degree of sorrow that they were so soon to leave them, which they showed by a more than usual degree of kindness and attention. The ship was crowded the whole day with the natives, and she was loaded with presents of coconuts, plantains, breadfruits, hogs, and goats."

Contrary to what had been the usual practice, there was that evening no dancing or mirth on the beach, such as they had long been accustomed to. All was silent.

At sunset, the boat returned from landing Tinah and his wife, and the ship made ready to sail, bidding farewell to Otaheite, where, Bligh observes, "for twenty-three weeks we had been treated with the utmost affection and regard, and which seemed to increase in proportion to our stay." He believed that the events which followed were caused by some of his crew's unwillingness to leave their island friends, and the pleasures of island life, behind.

CHAPTER FOUR
The Mutiny

"Thus far," says Bligh in his journal, "the voyage had advanced in a course of uninterrupted prosperity, and had been attended with many circumstances equally pleasing and satisfactory. A very different scene was now to be experienced. A conspiracy had been formed, which was to render all our past labour productive only of extreme misery and distress. The means had been concerted and prepared with so much secrecy and circumspection, that no one circumstance appeared to occasion the smallest suspicion of the impending calamity, the result of an act of piracy the most consummate and atrocious that was probably ever committed."

These are the facts of the mutiny, as stated by Bligh in his own words: "In the morning of the 28th April, the northwesternmost of the Friendly Islands, called Tofoa, bearing northeast, I was steering to the westward with a ship in most perfect order, all my plants in a most flourishing condition, and all my men and officers in good health. On leaving the deck I gave directions for the course to be steered during the night. The master had

the first watch; the gunner, the middle watch; and Mr Christian, the morning watch. This was the turn of duty for the night.

"Just before sun rising on Tuesday the 28th, while I was yet asleep, Mr Christian, officer of the watch, Charles Churchill, ship's corporal, John Mills, gunner's mate, and Thomas Burkitt, seaman, came into my cabin, and seizing me, tied my hands with a cord behind my back, threatening me with instant death if I spoke or made the least noise. I called, however, as loud as I could in hopes of assistance; but they had already secured the officers who were not of their party, by placing sentinels at their doors. There were three men at my cabin door, besides the four within; Christian had only a cutlass in his hand, the others had muskets and bayonets. I was hauled out of bed, and forced on deck in my shirt, suffering great pain from the tightness with which they had tied my hands behind my back, held by Fletcher Christian, and Charles Churchill, with a bayonet at my breast, and two men, Alexander Smith and Thomas Burkitt, behind me, with loaded muskets cocked and bayonets fixed. I demanded the reason of such violence, but received no other answer than abuse, for not holding my tongue. The master, the gunner, Mr Elphinstone, the master's mate, and Nelson, were kept confined below; and the fore hatchway was guarded by sentinels. The boatswain and car-

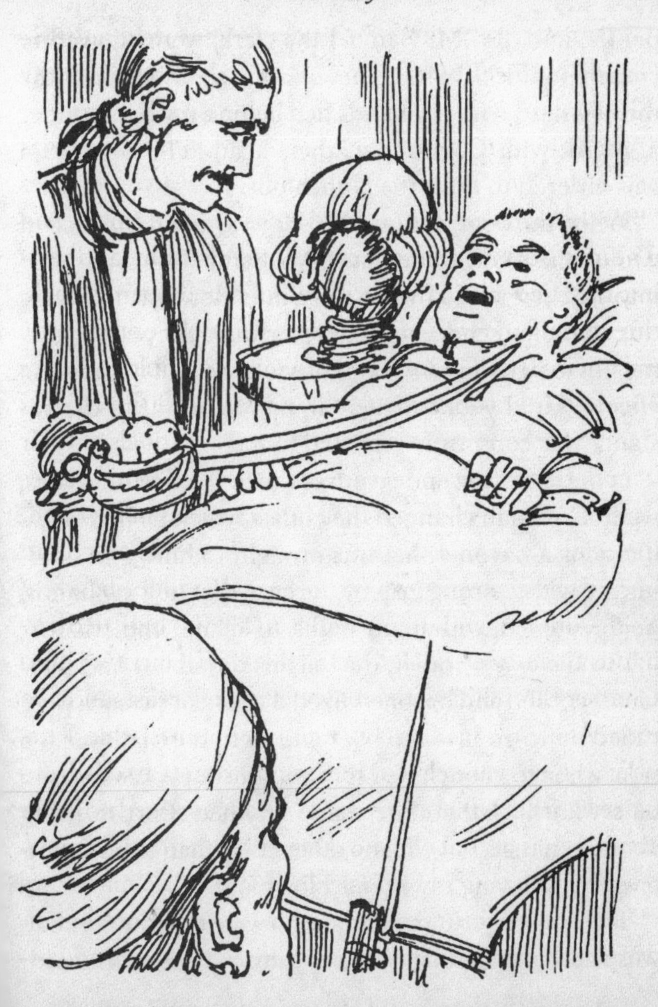

penter, and also Mr Samuel the clerk, were allowed to come upon deck, where they saw me standing abaft the mizzenmast, with my hands tied behind my back, under a guard, with Christian at their head. The boatswain was ordered to hoist the launch out.

"When the boat was out, Mr Hayward and Mr Hallet, two of the midshipmen, and Mr Samuel were ordered into it. I demanded what their intention was in giving this order, and endeavoured to persuade the people near me not to persist in such acts of violence; but it was to no effect - 'Hold your tongue, Sir, or you are dead this instant,' was constantly repeated to me.

"I continued my endeavours to turn the tide of affairs, when Christian changed the cutlass which he had in his hand for a bayonet that was brought to him, and holding me with a strong grip by the cord that tied my hands, he threatened, with many oaths, to kill me immediately, if I would not be quiet; the villains round me had their pieces cocked and bayonets fixed. Particular persons were called on to go into the boat and were hurried over the side; whence I concluded that with these people I was to be set adrift. I therefore made another effort to bring about a change, but with no other effect than to be threatened with having my brains blown out.

"The boatswain and seamen who were to go in the boat, were allowed to collect twine, canvas, lines, sails, cord-

age, an eight-and-twenty gallon cask of water; and Mr Samuel got one hundred and fifty pounds of bread, with a small quantity of rum and wine, also a quadrant and compass; but he was forbidden, on pain of death, to touch either map, ephemeris, book of astronomical observations, sextant, timekeeper, or any of my surveys or drawings.

"The mutineers having forced those of the seamen whom they meant to get rid of into the boat, Christian directed a dram to be served to each of his own crew. I then unhappily saw that nothing could be done to effect the recovery of the ship: there was no one to assist me, and every endeavour on my part was answered with threats of death.

"The officers were next called upon deck, and forced over the side into the boat, while I was kept apart from every one, abaft the mizzenmast, Christian, armed with a bayonet, holding me by the bandage that secured my hands. The guard round me had their pieces cocked, but on my daring the ungrateful wretches to fire, they uncocked them.

"Isaac Martin, one of the guard over me, I saw had an inclination to assist me, and as he fed me with shaddock (my lips being quite parched) we explained our wishes to each other by our looks; but this being observed, Martin was removed from me. He then attempted to leave the ship, for which purpose he got into the boat; but with

many threats they obliged him to return. The armourer, Joseph Coleman, and two of the carpenters, M'Intosh and Norman, were also kept, contrary to their inclination; and they begged of me, after I was astern in the boat, to remember that they declared they had no hand in the transaction. Michael Byrne, I am told, likewise wanted to leave the ship.

"I asked for arms, but they laughed at me, and said I was well acquainted with the people among whom I was going, and therefore did not want them; four cutlasses, however, were thrown into the boat, after we were veered astern.

"The officers and men being in the boat, they only waited for me, of which the master-at-arms informed Christian; who then said: 'Come, Captain Bligh, your officers and men are now in the boat, and you must go with them; if you attempt to make the least resistance, you will instantly be put to death'; and without further ceremony, with a tribe of armed ruffians about me, I was forced over the side, when they untied my hands. Being in the boat, we were veered astern by a rope, a few pieces of pork were thrown to us, and some clothes, also the cutlasses I have already mentioned; and it was then that the armourer and carpenters called out to me to remember that they had no hand in the transaction. After having undergone a great deal of ridicule, and been

kept for some time to make sport for these unfeeling wretches, we were at length cast adrift in the open ocean.

"I had with me in the boat the following persons:

Names	*Stations*
John Fryer	Master
Thomas Ledward	Acting Surgeon
David Nelson	Botanist
William Peckover	Gunner
William Cole	Boatswain
William Purcell	Carpenter
William Elphinstone	Master's Mate
Thomas Hayward	Midshipman
John Hallet	Midshipman
John Norton	Quartermaster
Peter Lenkletter	Quartermaster
Lawrence Lebogue	Sailmaker
John Smith	Cook
Thomas Hall	Cook
George Simpson	Quartermaster's Mate
Robert Tinkler	A Boy
Robert Lamb	Butcher
Mr Samuel	Clerk

– In all eighteen.

"There remained in the *Bounty*:

Names	*Stations*
Fletcher Christian	Master's Mate

Peter Heywood	Midshipman
Edward Young	Midshipman
George Stewart	Midshipman
Charles Churchill	Master-At-Arms
John Mills	Gunner's Mate
James Morrison	Boatswain's Mate
Thomas Burkitt	Able Seaman
Matthew Quintal	Able Seaman
John Sumner	Able Seaman
John Millward	Able Seaman
William M'Koy	Able Seaman
Henry Hillbrant	Cooper
Michael Byrne	Able Seaman
William Muspratt	Able Seaman
Alexander Smith	Able Seaman
John Williams	Able Seaman
Thomas Ellison	Able Seaman
Isaac Martin	Able Seaman
Richard Skinner	Able Seaman
Matthew Thompson	Able Seaman
William Brown	Gardener
Joseph Coleman	Armourer
Charles Norman	Carpenter's Mate
Thomas M'Intosh	Carpenter's Crew

– In all twenty-five – and the most able of the ship's company.

"Christian, the chief of the mutineers, is of a respectable family in the North of England. This was the third voyage he had made with me; and as I found it necessary to keep my ship's company at three watches, I had given him an order to take charge of the third, his abilities being thoroughly equal to the task. Heywood is also of a respectable family in the North of England, and a young man of abilities. Notwithstanding the roughness with which I was treated, the remembrance of past kindnesses produced some signs of remorse in Christian. When they were forcing me out of the ship, I asked him if this treatment was a proper return for the many instances he had received of my friendship? He appeared disturbed at my question, and answered with much emotion: 'That, Captain Bligh – that is the thing – I am in hell – I am in hell!'

"As soon as I had time to reflect, I felt an inward satisfaction, which prevented any depression of my spirits: conscious of my integrity, and anxious solicitude for the good of the service in which I had been engaged, I found my mind wonderfully supported, and I began to conceive hopes, notwithstanding so heavy a calamity, that I should one day be able to account to my king and country for the misfortune.

"It will very naturally be asked, what could be the reason for such a revolt? In answer to which I can only con-

jecture that the mutineers had flattered themselves with the hopes of a more happy life among the Otaheitans than they could possibly enjoy in England; and this, joined to some female connections, most probably occasioned the whole transaction. The ship, indeed, while within our sight, steered to the WNW, but I considered this only as a feint; for when we were sent away – 'Huzza for Otaheite!' – was frequently heard among the mutineers. The women of Otaheite are handsome, mild, and cheerful in their manners and conversation, possessed of great sensibility, and have sufficient delicacy to make them admired and beloved. The chiefs were so much attached to our people, that they rather encouraged their stay among them than otherwise, and even made them promises of large possessions. Under these and many other attendant circumstances, equally desirable, it is now perhaps not so much to be wondered at, that a set of sailors should be led away. Especially so, when, in addition to such powerful inducements, they imagined it in their power to fix themselves in the midst of plenty, on one of the finest islands in the world, where they need not labour, and where the allurements of dissipation are beyond anything that can be conceived. The utmost, however, that any commander could have supposed to have happened is, that some of the people would have been tempted to desert.

"Desertions have happened, more or less, from most of the ships that have been at the Society Islands; but it has always been in the commander's power to make the chiefs return their people; the knowledge, therefore, that it was unsafe to desert, perhaps first led mine to consider with what ease so small a ship might be surprised, and that so favourable an opportunity would never offer to them again.

"The secrecy of this mutiny is beyond all conception. Thirteen of the party, who were with me, had always lived forward among the seamen; yet neither they, nor the mess mates of Christian, Stewart, Heywood, and Young, had ever observed any circumstance that made them in the least suspect what was going on. To such a close-planned act of villainy, my mind being entirely free from any suspicion, it is not wonderful that I fell a sacrifice. Had their mutiny been occasioned by any grievances, either real or imaginary, I must have discovered symptoms of their discontent, which would have put me on my guard: but the case was far otherwise. Christian, in particular, I was on the most friendly terms with: that very day he was engaged to have dined with me; and the preceding night he excused himself from supping with me, on pretence of being unwell; for which I felt concerned, having no suspicions of his integrity and honour."

CHAPTER FIVE

The Reaction to Bligh's Story – A Different Version

Such is the story published by Lieutenant Bligh immediately on his return to England, after a difficult and dangerous journey of nearly four thousand miles across the wide ocean, with eighteen persons, in an open boat. The story obtained implicit credit, and although Lieutenant Bligh's character never stood high in the navy for smoothness of manners or mildness of temper, he was always considered an excellent seaman and his truthfulness was never doubted. But in this later age, when the most atrocious criminals find their apologists, it is not surprising it should now be suggested, when all are dead that could either prove or disprove it, that it was the tyranny of the commander alone, and not the wickedness of the ringleader of the mutineers, that caused the mutiny.

"We all know," says one critic of Bligh, "that mutiny can arise but from one of two sources, excessive folly or excessive tyranny; therefore, as it is admitted that Bligh was no idiot, the inference is obvious. Not only was the

THE JOURNAL of
LEUITENANT
William Bligh R.N.
Concerning
The Mutiny
on
HMS BOUNTY

narrative which he published proved to be false in many material bearings, by evidence before a court martial, but every act of his public life after this event was stamped with an insolence, an inhumanity, and coarseness, which fully developed his character."

There is no intention, in narrating this eventful history, to accuse or defend either the character or conduct of Admiral Bligh, as he became. It is well known his temper was irritable in the extreme, but he had been the friend of great men such as Captain Cook and Sir Joseph Banks. The Admiralty promoted him to the rank of commander and appointed him immediately to the *Providence*, to repeat the expedition to Otaheite, which met with complete success, and he recommended all his officers for promotion on account of their exemplary conduct. He rose to the rank of a flag officer. These things may perhaps speak in his favour and show that, for all his failings, he had his merits. That he was a man of coarse habits and entertained mistaken ideas about discipline is true. The accusation of Bligh having falsified his "narrative" is a heavy charge and is not wholly without foundation. It would perhaps be more correct to say that in the printed account of his voyage, *and the account on which the mutineers were tried*, there are many important omissions from his original manuscript journal. Some of these it will be necessary to look at presently.

In a manuscript journal kept by Morrison, the boatswain's mate, who was tried and convicted as one of the mutineers but received the king's pardon, the conduct of Bligh appears in a very unfavourable light.

It would appear from this document that the seeds of discord on board the *Bounty* were sown at a very early period of the voyage. As was the case in all small vessels, the duties of commander and purser were united in the person of Lieutenant Bligh, and it would seem that this proved the cause of very serious discontent among the officers and crew. At Tenerife, Lieutenant Bligh ordered the cheese to be hoisted up and exposed to the air, which was no sooner done than he pretended to miss a certain quantity and declared that it had been stolen. The cooper, Henry Hillbrant, informed him that the cask in question had been opened on the orders of Mr Samuel, his clerk, who acted also as steward, and the cheese sent on shore to his own house before the *Bounty* left the river on her way to Portsmouth. Lieutenant Bligh, without making any further inquiry, immediately ordered the allowance of cheese to be stopped, both from *officers* and *men*, until the deficiency should be made good, and told the cooper he would give him a d—d good flogging if he said another word on the subject.

Again, on approaching the Equator, some decayed pumpkins, purchased at Tenerife, were ordered to be is-

sued to the crew, at the rate of *one* pound of pumpkin for *two* pounds of biscuit. The reluctance of the men to accept this proposed substitute on such terms being reported to Lieutenant Bligh, he flew on deck in a violent rage, called out the crew and ordered the first man on the list of each mess to be called by name, at the same time saying: "I'll see who will dare to refuse the pumpkin, or anything else I may order to be served out;" to which he added: "You d—d infernal scoundrels, I'll make you eat grass, or anything you can catch, before I have done with you." This speech had the desired effect, all receiving the pumpkins, even the *officers*.

Next comes a complaint respecting the mode of issuing beef and pork. When a representation was made to Lieutenant Bligh in the quiet and orderly manner prescribed by the twenty-first Article of War, he called the crew aft, told them that everything to do with provisions was done by his orders and that it was therefore useless for them to complain as they would get no redress. He was the fittest judge of what was right or wrong, and he would flog the first man who dared to make any complaint in future. To this imperiousness they bowed in silence, and not another murmur was heard from them during the remainder of the voyage to Otaheite, it being their determination to seek legal redress on the *Bounty*'s return to England. Happy would it have been had they kept their reso-

lution. By so doing, if the story is true, they would amply have been avenged, a number of human lives spared and a world of misery avoided.

According to Morrison, "the seeds of eternal discord were sown between Lieutenant Bligh and some of his officers," while in Adventure Bay, Van Dieman's Land. On arriving at Matavai Bay, in Otaheite, Bligh is accused of taking the officers' pigs and breadfruit and serving them to the ship's company, and when the master remonstrated with him on the subject, he replied that "he would convince him that everything became *his* as soon as it was brought on board; that he would take nine-tenths of every man's property, and let him see who dared to say anything to the contrary." The sailors' pigs were seized without ceremony, and it became a favour for a man to obtain an extra pound of his own meat.

Morrison's journal records, "the object of our visit to the Society Islands being at length accomplished, we weighed on the 4th April 1789. Everyone seemed in high spirits, and began to talk of home, as though they had just left Jamaica instead of Otaheite, so far onward did their flattering fancies waft them. On the 23rd, we anchored off Annamooka, the inhabitants of which island were very rude, and attempted to take the casks and axes from the parties sent to fill water and cut wood. A musket pointed at them produced no other effect than a re-

turn of the compliment, by poising their clubs or spears with menacing looks; and, as it was Lieutenant Bligh's orders, that no person should affront them on any occasion, they were emboldened by meeting with no check to their insolence. They at length became so troublesome, that Mr Christian, who commanded the watering party, found it difficult to carry on his duty. On acquainting Lieutenant Bligh with their behaviour, he received a volley of abuse, was d—d as a cowardly rascal, and asked if he were afraid of naked savages whilst he had weapons in his hand? To this he replied in a respectful manner: 'The arms are of no effect, Sir, while your orders prohibit their use.'"

This happened only three days before the mutiny. That catastrophe, says Morrison, was hastened, if not brought about, by the following circumstance, which Bligh does not mention: "In the afternoon of the 27th, Lieutenant Bligh came upon deck, and missing some of the coconuts, which had been piled up between the guns, said they had been stolen, and could not have been taken away without the knowledge of the officers, all of whom were sent for and questioned on the subject. On their declaring that they had not seen any of the people touch them, he exclaimed, 'Then you must have taken them yourselves'; and proceeded to inquire of them separately, how many they had purchased. On coming to Mr Chris-

tian, that gentleman answered, 'I do not know, Sir, but I hope you do not think me so mean as to be guilty of stealing yours.' Mr Bligh replied: 'Yes, you d—d hound, I do – you must have stolen them from me, or you would be able to give a better account of them.' Then turning to the other officers, he said: 'God d—n you, you scoundrels, you are all thieves alike, and combine with the men to rob me: I suppose you will steal my yams next; but I'll sweat you for it, you rascals – I'll make half of you jump overboard, before you get through Endeavour Straits.' This threat was followed by an order to the clerk 'to stop the villains' grog, and give them but half a pound of yams tomorrow; if they steal them, I'll reduce them to a quarter.'"

It is difficult to believe that an officer in his Majesty's service would use such language to the meanest of the crew, much less to gentlemen, but it is to be feared that there is sufficient ground for the truth of these statements. With regard to the last, it is borne out by the evidence of Mr Fryer, the master, at the court martial. It was on the evening of this day that Lieutenant Bligh, according to his printed narrative, says Christian was to have supped with him but excused himself on account of being unwell; and that he was invited to dine with him on the day of the mutiny.

Every one of these circumstances, and many others,

noted in Morrison's journal, are omitted in Bligh's published narrative, but many of them are referred to in his original journal, and others that prove distinctly the constant reproofs to which his officers were subjected and the bad terms on which they stood with their commander. A few extracts from this journal will sufficiently establish this point.

In so early a part of the voyage as their arrival in Adventure Bay, he found fault with his officers, and put the carpenter into confinement. On the 5th January three men deserted in the cutter, on which occasion Bligh says: "Had the mate of the watch been awake, no trouble of this kind would have happened. I have therefore disrated and turned him before the mast; such neglectful and worthless petty officers, I believe, never were in a ship as are in this. No orders for a few hours together are obeyed by them, and their conduct in general is so bad, that no confidence or trust can be reposed in them; in short, they have driven me to every thing but corporal punishment, and that must follow if they do not improve."

By Morrison's journal it would appear that "corporal punishment" was not long delayed; for, on the very day, he says, the midshipman was put in irons and confined from the 5th January to the 23rd March–eleven weeks!

On the 24th January, the three deserters were brought back and flogged, then put in irons for further punish-

ment. "As this affair," Bligh says, "was solely caused by the neglect of the officers who had the watch, I was induced to give them all a lecture on this occasion, and endeavour to show them that, however exempt they were at present from the like punishment, yet they were equally subject, by the articles of war, to a condign one." He then tells them that it is only necessity that makes him lecture them because there are no means of trying them by court martial, and adds a remark, not very intelligible, but what he calls an unpleasant one, about *such* offenders having no feelings of honour or sense of shame.

Bligh wrote of his officers: "I have such a neglectful set about me, that I believe nothing but condign punishment can alter their conduct. Verbal orders, in the course of a month, were so forgotten, that they would impudently assert no such thing or directions were given, and I have been at last under the necessity to trouble myself with writing what, by decent young officers, would be complied with as the common rules of the service."

These extracts show the terms on which Bligh was with his officers. They make it pretty clear, that although Christian – as fiery and passionate a youth as his commander could well be, and with feelings too acute to bear the foul and offensive language constantly addressed to him – was the sole instigator of the mutiny, the captain had no support to expect, and certainly received none,

from the rest of his officers. That Christian was the sole author appears still more strongly from the following passage in Morrison's journal: "When Mr Bligh found he must go into the boat, he begged of Mr Christian to desist, saying: 'I'll pawn my honour, I'll give my bond, Mr Christian, never to think of this, if you'll desist,' and urged his wife and family; to which Mr Christian replied, 'No, Captain Bligh, if you had any honour, things had not come to this; and if you had any regard for your wife and family, you should have thought on them before, and not behaved so much like a villain.' Lieutenant Bligh again attempted to speak, but was ordered to be silent. The boatswain also tried to pacify Mr Christian, to whom he replied: 'It is too late, I have been in hell for this fortnight past, and am determined to bear it no longer; and you know, Mr Cole, that I have been used like a dog all the voyage.'"

It is pretty evident, therefore, that the mutiny was not, as Bligh in his narrative states it to have been, the result of a conspiracy. The whole affair was planned and executed between the hours of four and eight o'clock on the morning of the 28th April, when Christian had the watch upon deck. Christian, unable longer to bear the abusive and insulting language, had meditated his own escape from the ship the day before, choosing to trust himself to fate rather than submit to the constant cen-

sure to which he had been subject, but the unfortunate business of the coconuts drove him to the commission of the rash action, which ended, as such criminal acts usually do, in his own destruction and that of a great number of others, many of whom were wholly innocent.

Lieutenant Bligh, like most passionate men whose unruly tempers get the better of their reason, having vented his rage, became immediately calm, and, by inviting Christian to sup with him the same evening, evidently wished to renew their friendly intercourse; and happy would it have been for all parties had he accepted the invitation. On the same night, towards ten o'clock, when the master had the watch, Bligh came on deck, as was his custom, before retiring to sleep. It was one of those calm and beautiful nights, so frequent in tropical regions, whose soothing influence can be appreciated only by those who have felt it, when, after a scorching day, the air breathes a most refreshing coolness. It was an evening of this sort, when Bligh for the last time came on deck in the capacity of commander; a gentle breeze scarcely rippled the water, and the moon, then in its first quarter, shed its soft light along the surface of the sea.

Meanwhile, the unhappy and deluded Christian was, in all probability, brooding over his wrongs and meditating on the criminal act he was to perpetrate the following morning.

CHAPTER SIX
The Open-Boat Navigation

Christian had intended to send away his captain and associates in the cutter, and ordered that it should be hoisted out for that purpose. It was a small, wretched boat, so worm-eaten and decayed, especially in the bottom planks, that the probability was that she would have gone down before she had proceeded a mile from the ship. But the master, boatswain and carpenter prevailed on him to let those unfortunate men have the launch, into which nineteen persons were thrust, whose weight, together with that of the few articles they were permitted to take, brought down the boat so near to the water, as to endanger her sinking with but a moderate swell of the sea. To all appearances, it was in no state to survive the length of voyage that they were destined to travel over the wide ocean.

The first consideration of Lieutenant Bligh and his eighteen unfortunate companions was to examine the state of their resources. The quantity of provisions which they found to have been thrown into the boat, by some few kind-hearted mess mates, amounted to one hundred

and fifty pounds of bread, sixteen pieces of pork, each weighing two pounds, six quarts of rum, six bottles of wine, with twenty-eight gallons of water and four empty barricoes.

Being so near to the island of Tofoa, it was resolved to seek there a supply of breadfruit and water, to preserve if possible the above-mentioned stock entirely, but after rowing along the coast, they discovered only some coconut trees, on the top of high cliffs, from which, with much danger owing to the surf, and great difficulty in climbing the cliffs, they succeeded in obtaining about twenty nuts. The second day they made excursions into the island, but without success. They met, however, a few people of the island, who came down with them to the cove where the boat was lying, and others presently followed. They made inquiries after the ship, and Bligh unfortunately advised that they should say that the ship had sunk and that they were the only people saved. It was indiscreet to put the island's people in possession of their defenceless situation; however, they brought in small quantities of breadfruit, plantains and coconuts, but little or no water could be procured. These supplies, scanty as they were, served to keep up the spirits of the men.

The number of island people having so much increased as to line the whole beach, they began knocking stones together, which was known to be the preparatory signal

for an attack. With some difficulty, the seamen succeeded in getting the things that were on shore into the boat, together with all the men, except John Norton, quartermaster, who was casting off the stern-fast. The people immediately rushed on this poor man and actually stoned him to death. A volley of stones was also discharged at the boat, and everyone in it was more or less hurt. This made them push out to sea with all the speed they were able to give to the launch, but, to their surprise and alarm, several canoes filled with people with stones followed close after them and renewed the attack, against which the only return the unfortunate men in the boat could make was with the stones of the assailants that had landed in her, a type of warfare in which they were very inferior. The only measure left was to tempt the enemy to give up the pursuit by throwing overboard some clothes, which fortunately induced the canoes to stop and pick them up, and with night coming on, the canoes returned to the shore, leaving the party in the boat to reflect on their unhappy situation.

The men now pleaded with their commander to take them towards home, and on being told that no hope of relief could be entertained till they reached Timor, a distance of almost four thousand miles, they all readily agreed to be content with an allowance, which, the commander informed them, would not exceed one ounce of

bread and a quarter of a pint of water per day. Recommending them, therefore, in the most solemn manner, not to depart from their promise in this respect, "I was happy," says Bligh, "to see that everyone seemed better satisfied with our situation than myself."

At daybreak on the 3rd, they saw with alarm that the sun was rising fiery and red, a sure sign of a severe gale, and, accordingly, at eight o'clock it blew a violent storm, and the sea ran so very high that they were in very imminent danger and distress, the sea curling over the stern of the boat and obliging them to bale the water out of the launch with all their might.

The bread, being in bags of cloth, was in the greatest danger of being spoiled by the wet, the consequence of which, if not prevented, must have been fatal, as the whole party would inevitably have starved to death, even if they had escaped the fury of the waves. It was determined, therefore, that all superfluous clothes, with some rope and spare sails, should be thrown overboard. The carpenter's tool chest was emptied, and the tools stowed in the bottom of the boat, and the bread was put in the chest. All the people being thoroughly wet and cold, a teaspoonful of rum was served out to each, with a quarter of a breadfruit, which is stated to have been scarcely eatable, for dinner. The sea continued to run even higher than in the morning, and the fatigue of baling became

very great. The boat had to be kept before the sea, so the men were constantly wet. The night was very cold, and at daylight their limbs were so numb that they could scarcely use them. Five small coconuts were distributed for dinner, and everyone was satisfied; and in the evening, a few broken pieces of breadfruit were served for supper, after which prayers were performed.

After the gale had abated, the first step was to examine the state of the bread, a great part of which was found to be damaged and rotten – but even this was carefully preserved for use. The boat was now running among some islands, but after what had happened at Tofoa, they did not venture to land. On the 6th, they still continued to see islands at a distance; and on this day, for the first time, they hooked a fish, to their great joy – "but," says the commander, "we were miserably disappointed by its being lost in trying to get it into the boat."

Lieutenant Bligh observes, "it will readily be supposed our lodgings were very miserable, and confined for want of room". He tried to remedy the latter defect by putting them at watch and watch, so that one half of them always sat up, while the other lay down on the boat's bottom, or upon a chest, but with nothing to cover them except the heavens. Their limbs, he says, were dreadfully cramped for they could not stretch them out; and the nights were so cold, and they were so constantly wet,

that, after a few hours' sleep, they were scarcely able to move. Heavy rain came on, when every person in the boat did his utmost to catch some water, and thus succeeded in increasing their stock to thirty-four gallons, besides quenching their thirst for the first time since they had been at sea.

On the 8th, the allowance issued was an ounce and a half of pork, a teaspoonful of rum, half a pint of coconut milk and an ounce of bread. "Hitherto," Bligh says, "I had issued the allowance by guess, but I now made a pair of scales with two coconut shells; and having accidentally some pistol balls in the boat, twenty-five of which weighed one pound or sixteen ounces, I adopted one of these balls as the proportion of weight that each person should receive of bread at the times I served it. I also amused all hands with describing the situations of New Guinea and New Holland, and gave them every information in my power, that in case any accident should happen to me, those who survived might have some idea of what they were about, and be able to find their way to Timor, which at present they knew nothing of more than the name, and some not even that. The weather continued extremely bad, and the wind increased; we spent a very miserable night, without sleep, except such as could be got in the midst of rain."

Two days later, nothing had changed. "At daybreak I

served to every person a teaspoonful of rum, our limbs being so much cramped that we could scarcely move them. Our situation was now extremely dangerous, the sea frequently running over our stern, which kept us baling with all our strength. At noon the sun appeared, which gave us as much pleasure as is felt when it shows itself on a winter's day in England."

When each new day came, wrote Bligh, "it showed a miserable set of beings, full of wants, without any thing to relieve them. Some complained of great pain in their bowels, and every one of having almost lost the use of his limbs. The little sleep we got was in no way refreshing, as we were constantly covered with the sea and rain. The weather continuing, and no sun affording the least prospect of getting our clothes dried, I recommended to every one to strip and wring them through the sea water, by which means they received a warmth that, while wet with rain water, they could not have."

The shipping of seas and constant baling continued. and although the men were shivering with wet and cold, the commander was under the necessity of informing them that he could no longer afford them the regular comfort they had derived from the teaspoonful of rum.

On the morning of the 17th, at dawn of day, "I found," says the commander, "every person complaining, and some of them solicited extra allowance, which I posi-

tively refused. Our situation was miserable; always wet, and suffering extreme cold in the nights, without the least shelter from the weather. The little rum we had was of the greatest service: when our nights were particularly distressing, I generally served a teaspoonful or two to each person, and it was always joyful tidings when they heard of my intentions.

"I had the pleasure to see a fine morning produce some cheerful countenances; and for the first time, during the last fifteen days, we experienced comfort from the warmth of the sun. We stripped and hung up our clothes to dry, which were by this time become so threadbare, that they could not keep out either wet or cold. In the afternoon we had many sea-birds about us, which are never seen far from land, such as boobies and noddies."

As the sea now began to run fair and the boat shipped only a little water, Lieutenant Bligh took the opportunity to examine the state of their bread, and it was found that, according to the way they were living, there was a sufficient quantity remaining for twenty-nine days' allowance, by which time there was every reason to expect that they would be able to reach Timor. But as this was still uncertain, and it was possible that, after all, they might be obliged to go to Java, it was determined to proportion the allowance so as to make the stock hold out six weeks. "I was apprehensive," he says, "that this would

be ill received, and that it would require my utmost resolution to enforce it; for, small as the quantity was which I intended to take away for our future good, yet it might appear to my people like robbing them of life; and some who were less patient than their companions, I expected would very ill brook it. However, on my representing the necessity of guarding against delays that might be occasioned by contrary winds, or other causes, and promising to enlarge upon the allowance as we got on, they cheerfully agreed to my proposal." It was accordingly settled that every person should receive one twenty-fifth part of a pound of bread for breakfast, and the same quantity for dinner as usual, but that the proportion for supper should be discontinued; this arrangement left them forty-three days' consumption.

On the 25th, about noon, some noddies came so near to the boat that one of them was caught by hand. This bird was about the size of a small pigeon. "I divided it," says Bligh, "with its entrails, into eighteen portions, and by a well-known method at sea, of '*Who shall have this*?' One member of the crew faces away from the food being divided, and says who shall receive each share, without seeing which part is offered. With grim humour Bligh noted how the others laughed when in this way he himself received little more than the bird's beak and claws. With the allowance of bread and water for dinner, the

noddy was eaten up, bones and all, with salt water for sauce. "In the evening, several boobies flying very near to us, we had the good fortune to catch one of them. This bird is as large as a duck. They are the most presumptive proof of being near land, of any sea fowl we are acquainted with. I directed the bird to be killed for supper, and the blood to be given to three of the people who were the most distressed for want of food. The body, with the entrails, beak, and feet, I divided into eighteen shares, and with the allowance of bread, which I made a merit of granting, we made a good supper compared with our usual fare."

The weather was now serene, which, nevertheless, was not without its inconveniences, for, it appears, they began to feel distress of a different kind from that which they had hitherto been accustomed to suffer. The heat of the sun was now so powerful that several of the people were seized with a languor and faintness that seemed to threaten their deaths. But the little circumstance of catching two boobies in the evening, trifling as it may appear, had the effect of raising their spirits. The stomachs of these birds contained several flying fish and small cuttlefish, all of which were carefully saved to be divided for dinner the next day. They were then accordingly divided with their entrails, and the contents of their maws, into eighteen portions, and, as the prize was a very valuable

one, it was distributed as before, by calling out, "*Who shall have this*?" – "so that today," says the Lieutenant, "with the usual allowance of bread at breakfast and at dinner, I was happy to see that every person thought he had feasted." From the appearance of the clouds in the evening, Mr Bligh had no doubt they were then near the land, and the people amused themselves with conversing on the probability of what they would meet with on it.

CHAPTER SEVEN

A Landfall, and a Renewed Voyage

Accordingly, at one in the morning of the 28th, the man at the helm heard the sound of breakers. It was the "barrier reef" which runs along the eastern coast of New Holland (Queensland), through which it now became the anxious object to discover a passage. The idea of getting into smooth water and finding refreshment kept up the people's spirits. The sea broke furiously over the reef, but beyond the water was so smooth and calm that every man already anticipated the heartfelt satisfaction he would feel as soon as they had passed the barrier. At length a break in the reef was discovered, a quarter of a mile wide, and through this the boat passed with a strong stream running west and came immediately into smooth water – all the hardships seemed at once to be forgotten.

They now returned thanks to God for His generous protection, and with much content took their miserable allowance of the twenty-fifth part of a pound of bread, and a quarter of a pint of water, for dinner.

The coast now began to show itself very distinctly, and in the evening they landed on the sandy point of an island. The party sent out to reconnoitre returned highly pleased at having found plenty of oysters and fresh water. With the help of a small magnifying glass a fire was made, and among the things that had been thrown into the boat was a tinderbox and a piece of brimstone, so that in future they had the ready means of making a fire.

One of the men too had been so provident as to bring away with him from the ship a copper pot; and thus with a mixture of oysters, bread, and pork, a stew was made, of which each person received a full pint. The general complaints among them were dizziness in the head, great weakness in the joints and violent cramps of the bowels, but none of them is stated to have been alarming, and despite their sufferings from cold and hunger, all of them retained marks of strength.

Mr Bligh had cautioned them not to touch any kind of berry or fruit that they might find, yet it appears that they were no sooner out of sight than they began to eat freely the three different kinds that grew all over the island. The symptoms of having eaten too much began at last to frighten them. They fancied they were all poisoned and regarded each other with the strongest marks of apprehension, uncertain about what might happen. Fortunately the fruit proved to be wholesome and good.

With oysters and palm tops stewed together, they now had excellent meals, without using up any of their bread. In the morning of the 30th, Mr Bligh saw with delight a visible alteration in the men for the better, and he sent them away to gather oysters in order to carry a stock of them to sea, for he was determined to put off again that evening. They also obtained fresh water and filled all their vessels to the amount of nearly sixty gallons. On examining the bread, it was found that there was still about thirty-eight days' allowance.

Being now ready for sea, they were ordered to attend prayers, but just as they were beginning, about twenty naked men appeared, running and hallooing and beckoning the strangers to come to them. As each was armed with a spear or lance, it was thought prudent to hold no communication with them. The mariners now proceeded northwards, with the continent on their left and several islands and reefs on their right.

On the 3rd of June, the little boat and her brave crew once more launched into the open ocean.

The brief stay on land had put new heart into Bligh's companions. He wrote: "So much confidence gave me great pleasure, and I may venture to assert that to this cause our preservation is chiefly to be attributed. I encouraged everyone with hopes that eight or ten days would bring us to a land of safety; and, after praying to

God for a continuance of His most gracious protection, I served out an allowance of water for supper, and directed our course to the west southwest.

"In the morning of the 10th, after a very comfortless night, there was a visible alteration for the worse, in many of the people, which gave me great apprehensions. An extreme weakness, swelled legs, hollow and ghastly countenances, a more than common inclination to sleep, with an apparent debility of understanding, seemed to me the melancholy presages of an approaching death. The surgeon and Lebogue, in particular, were most miserable objects. I occasionally gave them a few teaspoonfuls of wine, out of the little that remained, which greatly assisted them. The hope of being able to accomplish the voyage was our principal support. The boatswain very innocently told me that he really thought I looked worse than any in the boat. The simplicity with which he uttered such an opinion amused me, and I returned him a better compliment."

On the 11th Lieutenant Bligh announced to his companions that he had no doubt that they had now passed the meridian of the eastern part of Timor, a piece of intelligence that spread universal joy and satisfaction. And, sure enough, at three in the morning of the following day, Timor was discovered at the distance of only six miles from the shore.

"It is not possible for me," says this experienced navigator, "to describe the pleasure which the blessing of the sight of this land diffused among us. It appeared scarcely credible to ourselves that, in an open boat, and so poorly provided, we should have been able to reach the coast of Timor in forty-one days after leaving Tofoa, having in that time run by our log, a distance of three thousand six hundred and eighteen nautical miles; and that, notwithstanding our extreme distress, no one should have perished in the voyage."

On Sunday the 14th they anchored safely in Coupang Bay, where they were received with kindness, hospitality and humanity. The houses of the principal people were thrown open to them. The poor sufferers when landed were scarcely able to walk; their condition is described as most deplorable. "The abilities of a painter could rarely, perhaps, have been displayed to more advantage than in the delineation of the two groups of figures which at this time presented themselves to each other," noted Bligh. "An indifferent spectator (if such could be found) would have been at a loss which most to admire, the eyes of famine sparkling at immediate relief, or the horror of their preservers at the sight of so many spectres, whose ghastly countenances, if the cause had been unknown, would rather have excited terror than pity. Our bodies were nothing but skin and bones, our limbs were full of

sores, and we were clothed in rags; in this condition, with the tears of joy and gratitude flowing down our cheeks, the people of Timor beheld us with a mixture of horror, surprise, and pity."

Having recruited their strength by a residence of two months among the friendly inhabitants of Coupang, they travelled to the westward on the 20th August in a small schooner that was bought and armed for the purpose, and arrived on the 1st October in Batavia Road (Jakarta, in Java). There Mr Bligh embarked in a Dutch packet, and was landed on the Isle of Wight on the 14th March 1790. The rest of the people had passages provided for them in ships of the Dutch East India Company, then about to sail for Europe.

We may go further and say that it is impossible to read about this extraordinary voyage without bestowing unqualified praise on the able and wise conduct of its commander, who is in every respect, as far as this extraordinary enterprise is concerned, fully entitled to rank with Parry, Franklin and Richardson. Few men, indeed, were ever placed for so long a period in a more trying, distressing and perilous situation than he was. It may safely be attributed to his discreet management of the men and their scanty resources and his ability as a thorough seaman that eighteen souls were saved from imminent and otherwise inevitable destruction.

CHAPTER EIGHT

The Pandora Sets Out to Find the Mutineers

The tide of public opinion was running very much in favour of Bligh, on account of his sufferings and the successful issue of his daring voyage. Heavy indignation was launched against Christian and his associates for the audacious and criminal deed they had committed. Bligh was promoted by the Admiralty to the rank of Commander and speedily sent out a second time to transport the breadfruit to the West Indies, which he successfully accomplished. His Majesty's government were no sooner made aware of the atrocious act of piracy and mutiny of the *Bounty* than it determined to adopt every possible means to capture the guilty men and punish them. For this purpose, the *Pandora* frigate, with twenty-four guns and one hundred and sixty men, was dispatched under the command of Captain Edward Edwards, with orders to proceed to Otaheite and use his best endeavours to seize and bring home in confinement the whole or such part of the mutineers as he might be able to discover.

This voyage turned out almost as disastrous as that of the *Bounty*, but from a different cause. The waste of human life was much greater, occasioned by the wreck of the ship, and the distress experienced by the crew not much less, owing to the famine and thirst they had to suffer in a navigation of eleven hundred miles in open boats; but the Captain succeeded in fulfilling a part of his instructions, by taking prisoner fourteen of the mutineers, of whom ten were brought safely to England, the other four being drowned when the ship was wrecked.

Many abusive names have been given to Captain Edwards, and observations made on the conduct of this officer highly harmful to his reputation, in regard to his inhuman treatment of his prisoners. The evidence suggests that these observations are all too true.

The account of Captain Edwards's proceedings, rendered by himself to the Admiralty, is vague and unsatisfactory. Had it not been for the journal of Morrison and a circumstantial letter of young Heywood to his mother, no record would have remained of the unfeeling conduct of this officer towards his unfortunate prisoners, who were treated with a rigour that could not be justified on any ground of necessity or prudence.

The *Pandora* anchored in Matavai Bay on the 23rd March 1791. Captain Edwards, in his narrative, states that Joseph Coleman, the armourer of the *Bounty*, at-

tempted to come on board before the *Pandora* had anchored. On Coleman's reaching the ship, the captain began to make inquiries of him after the *Bounty* and her people, and he seemed to be ready to give him any information that was required. The next who came on board, just after the ship had anchored, were Mr Peter Heywood and Mr Stewart, who, like Coleman, made their way out before any boat had been sent to shore. These two were brought down to Edwards's cabin. After some conversation, Heywood asked if Mr Hayward (midshipman of the *Bounty* but now lieutenant of the *Pandora*) was on board, as he had heard that he was. Lieutenant Hayward, when sent for, treated Heywood with a sort of contemptuous look and began to enter into conversation with him respecting the *Bounty*; but Edwards ordered him to stop and called in the sentry to take the prisoners into safe custody and put them in irons. Four other mutineers soon appeared, and from them and some of the island people, he learned that the rest of the *Bounty*'s people had built a schooner, with which they had sailed only the day before from Matavai Bay to the northwest part of the island.

Captain Edwards goes on to say that, on this intelligence, he sent the two lieutenants, Corner and Hayward, with the pinnace and launch, to try to intercept her. They soon got sight of her and chased her out to sea, but the

schooner gained so much upon them, and night coming on, they were compelled to give up their pursuit and return to the ship. It was soon made known, however, that she had returned to Paparré, on which news they were again sent in search of her. Lieutenant Corner had captured three of the mutineers, and Hayward, on arriving at Paparré, found the schooner there, but the mutineers had abandoned her and fled to the mountains. He carried off the schooner, and returned next day, when he learned that they were not far off. The following morning he called to them to lay down their arms, which they did, and they were brought as prisoners to the ship.

The following were the persons received on board the *Pandora*:

Peter Heywood	Thomas Ellison
George Stewart	Henry Hillbrant
James Morrison	Thomas Burkitt
Charles Norman	John Millward
Thomas M'Intosh	John Sumner
Joseph Coleman	William Muspratt
Richard Skinner	Michael Byrne

– in all fourteen. The other two, which made up the sixteen that had been left on the island, had been murdered, as will appear presently.

Captain Edwards will himself explain how he disposed of his prisoners. "I put the pirates," he says, "into a round-

house which I built on the after part of the quarterdeck, for their more effectual security in this airy and healthy situation, and to separate them from, and to prevent their having communication with, or to crowd and incommode, the ship's company."

Dr Hamilton calls it the most desirable place in the ship, and adds, that "orders were given that the prisoners should be victualled, in every respect, the same as the ship's company, both in meat, liquor, and all the extra indulgences with which they were so liberally supplied, notwithstanding the established laws of the service, which restrict prisoners to two-thirds allowance; but Captain Edwards very humanely commiserated their unhappy and inevitable length of confinement."

Mr Morrison, one of the prisoners, gives a very different account of their treatment from that of Edwards or Hamilton. He says that Captain Edwards put both legs of the two midshipmen in irons and that he branded them "piratical villains": that they, with the rest, being strongly handcuffed, were put into a kind of roundhouse only eleven feet long, built as a prison, and aptly named "*Pandora*'s Box," which was entered by a scuttle in the roof, about eighteen inches square. This was done in order that they might be kept separate from the crew, and also the more effectively to prevent them from having any communication with the island people. Such of

those friendly people as ventured to look pitifully towards them were instantly turned out of the ship, and never again allowed to come on board. But two sentries were kept constantly on the roof of the prison, with orders to shoot the first of its inmates who attempted to address another in the Otaheitan dialect.

That Captain Edwards took every precaution to keep his prisoners in safe custody may be well imagined, but Mr Morrison will probably be thought to go somewhat beyond credibility in stating that orders were given "to *shoot* any of the prisoners," when confined in irons. Captain Edwards must have known that such an act would have cost him his commission or something more. The fact is that information was given to Edwards, at least he so asserts, by the brother of the king of Otaheite, an intelligent chief, that a conspiracy was formed among the island people to cut the ship's cables in the first strong wind that should blow on the shore. This action was considered to be the more probable as many of the prisoners were said to be married to the most respectable chiefs' daughters in the district opposite to the anchorage; that the midshipman Stewart, in particular, had married the daughter of a man of great landed property near Matavai Bay. This intelligence, no doubt, weighed with the Captain in giving his orders for the close confinement of the prisoners and particularly in restricting the visits of the

Otaheiteans. But so far is it from being true that all communication between the mutineers and the Otaheiteans was cut off that we are distinctly told by Hamilton that "the prisoners' wives visited the ship daily, and brought their children, who were permitted to be carried to their unhappy fathers. To see the poor captives in irons, weeping over their tender offspring, was too moving a scene for any feeling heart. Their wives brought them ample supplies of every delicacy that the country afforded, while we lay anchored there, and behaved with the greatest fidelity and affection towards them."

All the mutineers who were left on the island having been received on board the *Pandora*, that ship then went in search of those who had gone away in the *Bounty*. It may be mentioned, however, that two of the most active in the mutiny, Churchill and Thompson, had perished on the island before her arrival, by violent deaths. A chief, who was the *tayo*, or sworn friend, of Churchill, having died without children, this mutineer succeeded to his property and title, according to the custom of the country. Thompson, for some real or fancied insult, took an opportunity of shooting his companion. The Otaheiteans assembled, came to a resolution to avenge the murder and literally stoned Thompson to death, and his skull was brought on board the *Pandora*.

Captain Edwards had no clue to guide him as to the

route taken by the *Bounty*, but he learnt from different people and from journals kept on board that ship, which were found in the chests of the mutineers at Otaheite, the proceedings of Christian and his associates after Lieutenant Bligh and his companions had been turned adrift in the launch.

From these, it appears that the mutineers proceeded in the first instance to the island of Toobouai, where they anchored on the 25th May 1789. They had thrown overboard the greater part of the breadfruit plants and divided among themselves the property of the officers and men who had been turned adrift. At this island they intended to form a settlement, but the opposition of the island people, the lack of many necessary materials and quarrels among themselves determined them to go to Otaheite to obtain what might be needed to bring about their purpose. They accordingly sailed from Toobouai about the latter end of the month and arrived at Otaheite on the 6th June.

The Otoo, or reigning sovereign, and other principal people were very inquisitive and anxious to know what had become of Lieutenant Bligh and the rest of the crew, and also what had been done with the breadfruit plants. They were told they had most unexpectedly fallen in with Captain Cook at an island he had just discovered, called Whytootakee, where he intended to form a settlement,

and where the plants had been landed, and that Lieutenant Bligh and the others were stopping there to assist Captain Cook in the business he had in hand, and that he had appointed Mr Christian commander of the *Bounty*; and that he was now come by his orders for an additional supply of pigs, goats, fowls, breadfruit and various other articles that Otaheite could supply.

This artful story was quite enough to make these humane and simple-minded islanders believe the mutineers, and so overcome with joy were they to hear that their old friend Captain Cook was alive and about to settle so near them that every possible means were forthwith made use of to obtain the things that were wanted, so that in the course of a very few days the *Bounty* received on board three hundred and twelve pigs, thirty-eight goats, eight dozen fowls, a bull and a cow, and a large quantity of breadfruit, plantains, bananas and other fruits. They also took with them eight men, nine women and seven boys. With these supplies they left Otaheite on the 19th June and arrived a second time at Toobouai on the 26th. They warped the ship up the harbour, landed the livestock and set about building a fort of fifty yards square.

While this work was carrying on, quarrels and disagreements were daily happening among them, and continual disputes and skirmishes were taking place with the island people. The situation of the mutineers became so

disagreeable and unsafe, the work went on so slowly and reluctantly that the building of the fort was agreed to be discontinued. Christian, in fact, had very soon seen that his authority was on the wane and that no peaceful establishment was likely to be accomplished at Toobouai. He therefore held a consultation as to what would be the most advisable step to take. After much angry discussion, it was decided that Toobouai should be abandoned, that the ship should once more be taken to Otaheite and that those who might choose to go on shore there might do so, and those who preferred to remain in the ship might go in her to whatever place they should agree on among themselves.

They sailed from Toobouai on the 15th and arrived at Matavai Bay on the 20th September 1789. Here sixteen of the mutineers were put on shore, at their own request, fourteen of whom were later taken on board the *Pandora*, and two of whom, as before mentioned, were murdered on the island. The remaining nine agreed to continue in the *Bounty*. The small arms, powder, canvas and the stores belonging to the ship were equally divided among the whole crew. The *Bounty* sailed finally from Otaheite on the night of the 21st September, and was last seen the following morning to the northwest of Point Venus. They took with them seven Otaheitan men and twelve women. Christian had frequently been heard to say that his ob-

ject was to discover some unknown or uninhabited island in which there was no harbour for shipping, where he would run the *Bounty* on shore and make use of her materials to form a settlement, but this was the only account, vague as it was, that could be obtained to direct Captain Edwards in his intended search.

It appears that when the schooner, of which we have spoken, had been finished, six of the fourteen mutineers who were left on Otaheite embarked in her with the intention of going to the East Indies and actually put to sea, but meeting with bad weather and suspecting the nautical abilities of Morrison, whom they had elected as commanding officer, they decided to return to Otaheite. Morrison, it seems, first undertook the construction of this schooner, being himself a tolerable mechanic, in which he was assisted by the two carpenters, the cooper and some others. Conscious of his innocence as far as the mutiny was concerned, his object is stated to have been that of reaching Batavia in time to secure a passage home in the next fleet bound to Holland. He claimed that their return was brought about not by any distrust of his own talents but by a refusal on the part of the island people to give them enough matting and other necessaries for so long a voyage. The people wanted to keep them on the island.

Stewart and young Heywood took no part in this trans-

action, having made up their minds to stay at Otaheite, there to await the arrival of a king's ship, it being certain that one would be sent out to search for them, whatever might have been the fate of Bligh and his companions. That this was really their intention is evident by the speed that they displayed in getting on board the *Pandora*, the moment of her arrival.

On the 8th of May, the frigate left Otaheite, accompanied by the little schooner that the mutineers had built. The *Pandora* called at numerous islands without success, but Lieutenant Corner, having landed on one of the islands in Palmerston group, found a yard and some spars with the broad arrow on them, marked *Bounty*. This induced the captain to search in all these islands, in the course of which the *Pandora*, having been driven out to sea by blowing weather, lost sight of the little tender and a jolly boat, the latter of which was never more heard of. After a fruitless search of three months, the *Pandora* arrived, on the 29th August, on the coast of New Holland, close to that extraordinary reef of coral rocks, called the Barrier Reef, which runs along the greater part of the eastern coast. There the ship ran aground on an outlying reef, and it soon became apparent that she could not be saved.

Eighty-nine of the ship's company and ten of the mutineers who had been prisoners on board survived the

wreck, but thirty-one of the ship's company and four mutineers were lost with the ship. Captain Edwards appears to have given little consideration to the welfare of the prisoners when the ship hit the rocks. The account of the wreck by Lieutenant Corner suggests that Captain Edwards indeed deserved the character given him of altogether lacking the common feelings of humanity.

As the ship gradually sank deeper, the prisoners remained chained in the roundhouse while the crew made their escape. It was only the humanity of the frigate's master-at-arms, who passed the keys of the leg-irons through the bars, that enabled some of the prisoners to escape. Four of them were drowned, still shackled to the walls of their prison. "On this melancholy occasion Mr Heywood was the last person but three who escaped from the prison, into which the water had already found its way through the bulkhead scuttles. Jumping overboard, he seized a plank, and was swimming towards a small sandy quay (key) about three miles distant, when a boat picked him up, and conveyed him thither in a state of nudity."

This account would appear almost incredible. It is true that men are sometimes found to act inhumanely, but then they are generally moved by some motive or extraordinary excitement; here, however, there was neither. On the contrary, the condition of the poor prisoners ap-

pealed most forcibly to the mercy and humanity of their jailor. The surgeon of the ship states, in his account of her loss, that as soon as the spars, booms, hen coops and other buoyant articles were cut loose, "the prisoners were ordered to be let out of irons." One would imagine, indeed, that the officers in this dreadful emergency would not be witness to such inhumanity without protesting against keeping these unfortunate men confined a moment beyond the period when it became evident that the ship must sink. It will be seen, however, presently, from Mr Heywood's own statement, that they were so kept and that the brutal and unfeeling conduct that has been imputed to Captain Edwards is only too true.

On the 7th November they arrived at Batavia, where Captain Edwards agreed with the Dutch East India Company to divide the whole of the ship's company and prisoners among four of their ships going to Europe. The latter the captain took with him in the *Vreedenburgh*; but finding his Majesty's ship *Gorgon* at the Cape, he transhipped himself and prisoners, and proceeded in her to Spithead, where he arrived on the 19th June 1792.

Captain Edwards, in his meagre narrative, takes no more notice of his prisoners with regard to the mode in which they were disposed of at Coupang and Batavia than he does when the *Pandora* went down. There seems to have been a general feeling at and before the court

martial that Captain Edwards had exercised a harsh, unnecessary and undue degree of severity on his prisoners. It is the custom, sanctioned no doubt by long usage, to place in irons all who may have been guilty of mutiny in a ship of war, and the necessity of so doing is obvious enough – to prevent in the most effective way communication with the rest of the ship's company, who might be affected by dealings with such rebellious men. Mutiny in those days was a crime so serious that, if found guilty, those who committed it had little hope of escaping the punishment of death. Such was the punishment to which a mutineer must, by the naval Articles of War, be sentenced. No alternative was given to a court martial in such a case but to pronounce a sentence either of acquittal or of death.

In the present case, however, most of the prisoners had surrendered themselves. Many of them had taken no active part in the mutiny, and others had been forcibly compelled to remain in the ship. It was not likely, therefore, that any danger could arise from indulging them occasionally, and in turns, with a few hours of fresh air on deck. Perhaps the circumstance of the crime of piracy, being added to that of mutiny, may have operated on Captain Edwards's stern nature and induced him to inflict a greater severity of punishment than he might otherwise have done.

On the second day after the arrival of the *Gorgon* at Spithead the prisoners were transferred to the *Hector*, commanded by Captain Montague, where they were treated with great humanity and allowed every indulgence that could, within reason, be extended to men in their unhappy situation until the period when they were to be arraigned before the competent authority and put on their trials for mutiny and piracy, which did not take place until the month of September.

CHAPTER NINE

The Court Martial

"If any person in or belonging to the fleet shall make, or endeavour to make, any mutinous assembly, upon any pretence whatsoever, every person offending herein, and being convicted thereof, by the sentence of the Court martial, shall suffer Death."

Naval Articles of War, Art. 19.

The Court assembled to try the prisoners on board His Majesty's ship *Duke*, on the 12th September 1792 and continued by adjournment from day to day (Sunday excepted) until the 18th of that month. Vice-Admiral Lord Hood presided over the court martial, with eleven senior captains. The charges set forth that Fletcher Christian, who was mate of the *Bounty*, assisted by others of the inferior officers and men, armed with muskets and bayonets, had violently and forcibly taken that ship from her commander, Lieutenant Bligh.

Mr Fryer, the master of the *Bounty*, was the first to be sworn in, and he testified as follows: That he had the first watch; that between ten and eleven o'clock Mr Bligh came on deck, according to custom, and after a short

conversation, and having given his orders for the night, left the deck; that at twelve he was relieved by the gunner and retired, leaving all quiet; that at dawn of day he was greatly alarmed by an unusual noise; and that, on attempting to jump up, John Sumner and Matthew Quintal laid their hands upon him, saying he was their prisoner; that on expostulating with them, he was told, "Hold your tongue, or you are a dead man, but if you remain quiet there is none on board will hurt a hair of your head". He further testified that on raising himself on the locker, he saw on the ladder, going up on deck, Mr Bligh in his shirt, with his hands tied behind him, and Christian holding him by the cord; that the master-at-arms, Churchill, then came to his cabin and took a brace of pistols and a hanger (sword), saying, "I will take care of these, Mr Fryer".

Mr Fryer asked, on seeing Mr Bligh bound, what they were going to do with the captain, and stated that Sumner replied, "D—n his eyes, put him into the boat, and let the —— see if he can live upon three-fourths of a pound of yams a day." The master claimed that he remonstrated with such conduct, but in vain. They said Bligh must go in the small cutter. "The small cutter!" Mr Fryer exclaimed. "Why her bottom is almost out, and very much eaten by the worms!" to which Sumner and Quintal both said, "D—n his eyes, the boat is too good for him."

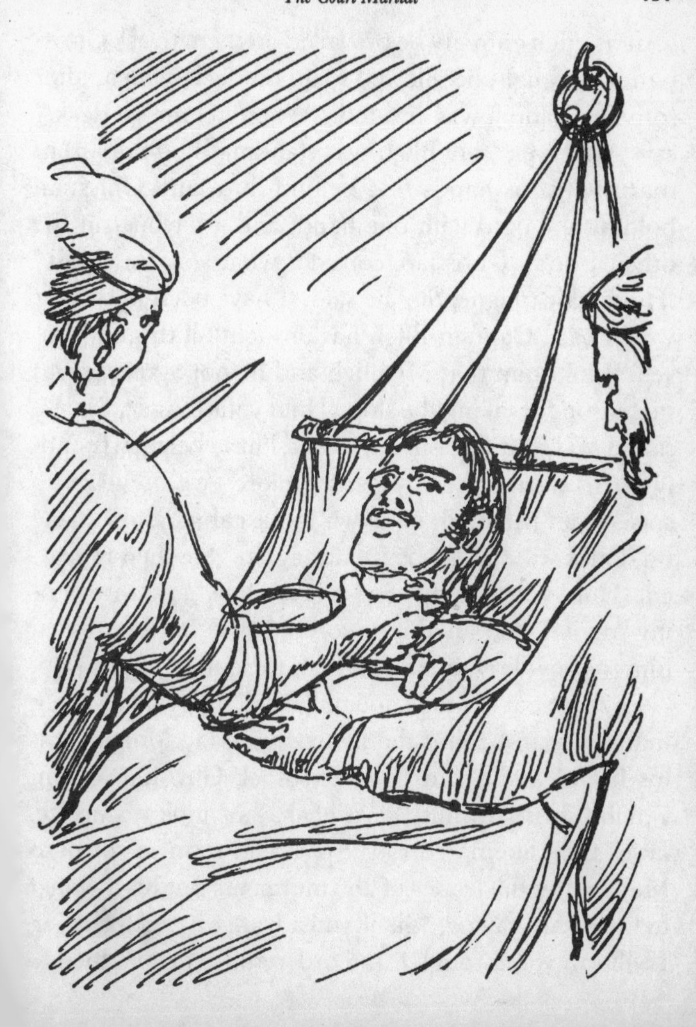

After much entreaty he prevailed on them to ask Christian if he might be allowed to go on deck, which, after some hesitation, was granted. "When I came on deck," says Mr Fryer, "Mr Bligh was standing by the mizzen-mast, with his hands tied behind him, and Christian holding the cord with one hand, and a bayonet in the other. I said, 'Christian, consider what you are about.' 'Hold your tongue, Sir,' he said; 'I have been in hell for weeks past; Captain Bligh has brought all this on himself.' I told him that Mr Bligh and he not agreeing was no reason for taking the ship. 'Hold your tongue, Sir,' he said. I said, 'Mr Christian, you and I have been on friendly terms during the voyage, therefore give me leave to speak – let Mr Bligh go down to his cabin, and I make no doubt we shall all be friends again.' He then repeated, 'Hold your tongue, Sir; it is too late,' and threatening me if I said anything more." Mr Fryer then asked him to provide a better boat than the cutter, but he said, "No, that boat is good enough." Bligh now said to Fryer, that the man behind the hencoops (Isaac Martin) was his friend and asked Fryer to knock Christian down, which Christian must have heard but took no notice. Fryer then attempted to get past Christian to speak to Martin, but the leader of the mutineers put his bayonet to his breast, saying, "Sir, if you advance an inch farther, I will run you through," and ordered two armed men to

take him down to his cabin. Shortly afterwards he was asked to go on deck, when Christian ordered him into the boat. He said, "I will stay with you, if you will give me leave." "No, Sir," Christian replied "go directly into the boat." Bligh, then on the gangway, said "Mr Fryer, stay in the ship." "No, by G—d, Sir," Christian said, "go into the boat, or I will run you through."

Mr Fryer states that during this time very bad language was used by the people towards Mr Bligh; that with great difficulty they persuaded Christian to allow a few articles to be put into the boat; that after the persons were ordered into the boat to the number of nineteen, such bad language continued to be used, several of the men calling out, "Shoot the ——." He heard Cole, the boatswain, advise that they should cast off and take their chance, as the mutineers would certainly do them a mischief if they stayed much longer. Mr Fryer then states the names of those who were under arms; and that Joseph Coleman, Thomas M'Intosh, Charles Norman and Michael Byrne (prisoners) wished to come into the boat, declaring they had nothing to do in the business; and that he did not see Mr Peter Heywood on deck at the seizure of the ship.

On being asked what he supposed Christian meant when he said he had been in hell for a fortnight, he said, from the frequent quarrels that they had and the abuse

he had received from Mr Bligh, and that the day before the mutiny Mr Bligh had accused all the young officers and sailors of stealing his coconuts.

Mr Cole, the boatswain, testified as follows: That he had the middle watch; was awakened out of his sleep in the morning, and heard a man calling out to the carpenter, that they had mutinied and taken the ship; that Christian had the command, and that the captain was a prisoner on the quarterdeck. He went up the hatchway, having seen Mr Heywood and Mr Young in the opposite berth; coming on deck he saw the captain with his hands tied behind him, and four guards standing over him, two of which were Ellison and Burkitt, the prisoners. The boatswain asked Mr Christian what he meant to do, and was answered by his ordering him to hoist the boat out and, shaking the bayonet, threatening him and damning him if he did not take care. When he found the captain was to be sent out of the ship, he again went aft with the carpenter to ask for the longboat; they asked three or four times before he granted it.

Cole stated that he saw Mr Peter Heywood, one of the prisoners, lending a hand to get the forestay fall along, and when the boat was hooked on, spoke something to him, but what it was he did not know, as Christian was threatening him at the time. Heywood then went below, and Cole did not remember seeing him afterwards. Af-

ter the few things were put into the boat, and most of the people in her, they were trying for the carpenter's tool chest, when Quintal said, "D—n them, if we let them have these things they will build a vessel in a month," but when all were in the boat she was veered astern, while Coleman, Norman and M'Intosh, prisoners, were crying at the gangway, wishing to go in the boat; and Byrne in the cutter alongside was also crying; that he advised Mr Bligh to cast off, as he feared the mutineers would fire into the boat.

The Court asked if he had any reason to believe that any other of the prisoners than those named were detained against their wishes? He answered: "I believe Mr Heywood was; I thought all along he was intending to come away; he had no arms, and he assisted to get the boat out and then went below; I heard Churchill call out, 'Keep them below.'" The Court: "Do you think he meant Heywood?" "I have no reason to think any other."

Lieutenant Thomas Hayward, late third lieutenant of the *Pandora* and formerly midshipman of the *Bounty*, testified as follows: That he had the morning watch; that at four o'clock Fletcher Christian relieved the watch as usual; that at five he ordered him, as master's mate of his watch, to look out while he went down to lash his hammock up; and that while he was looking at a shark astern of the ship, to his complete surprise, the decks now be-

came thronged with armed men. He saw that Peter Heywood, James Morrison (two of the prisoners) and George Stewart were unarmed on the booms. He affirmed that Fletcher Christian and his gang had not been down long before he heard the cry of murder from Lieutenant Bligh and Churchill calling out for a rope, on which Mills, contrary to all orders and entreaties, cut the deep-sea line and carried a piece of it to their assistance. Soon afterwards, Lieutenant Bligh was brought on to the quarterdeck with his hands bound behind him, and was surrounded by most of those who came last on deck.

Mr Cole being examined, gave his testimony: That he never saw Mr Heywood armed; that he did not consider him of the mutineers' party; that he saw nothing of levity or apparent merriment in his conduct; that when he was below with Stewart, he heard Churchill call out, "Keep them below," and that he believed Heywood was one of the persons meant – had no doubt of it at all. He affirmed to the Court that he by no means considered Heywood or Morrison as mutineers.

Mr Purcell, being examined, stated that, respecting the cutlass on which he saw Mr Heywood's hand resting, he did not consider him as being an armed man; and that he never thought of him as of the mutineers' party. He never heard Captain Bligh speak to Heywood and

thought, from Heywood's situation on the boom, that he could not have heard him in any case; and that Heywood was by no means guilty of levity or apparent merriment. He confirmed that he had heard the master-at-arms call out to keep them below; that Mr Hallet appeared to him to be very much confused; and that Mr Hayward likewise appeared to be very much confused.

The Court asked: "As you say you did not look upon the prisoner as a person armed, to what did you allude when you exclaimed, 'Good God, Peter, what do you do with that?'" The witness replied: "I look upon it as an accidental thing."

Mr Fryer was again called in and examined by Mr Morrison. Mr Fryer stated that he saw Morrison assist in hoisting out the boats; that he said to him (Fryer), "Go down below." The Court asked, "Whether it might not have been from a laudable motive, as supposing your assistance at that time might have prevented a more advantageous effort?" The witness replied: "Probably it might; had I stayed in the ship, he would have been one of the first that I should have opened my mind to, from his good behaviour in the former part of the voyage". Fryer affirmed his belief that Morrison had been giving him advice rather than an order and that, in hoisting out the boat, Morrison was helping Captain Bligh.

Mr Cole, the boatswain, stated that he ordered

Morrison to go and help them with the cutter; that Morrison told him that the boat was overloaded; that Captain Bligh had begged that no more people should go in her, and said he would take his chance in the ship; that he shook Morrison by the hand and said he would do him justice in England, and that he had no reason to suppose him concerned in the mutiny.

It is not necessary to note any parts of the defence made by the prisoners Coleman, Norman and M'Intosh as it is clear, from the whole evidence and from Bligh's certificates, that those men were anxious to go in the boat but were kept in the ship by force. It is equally clear that Ellison, Millward and Burkitt were concerned in every stage of the mutiny and had little to offer in their defence in exculpation of the crime of which they were accused.

On the sixth day of the court martial, the 18th September 1792, the Court met, and the prisoners were brought in. After the presiding officer had asked the prisoners if they or any one of them had anything more to offer in their defence, the Court was cleared, and it was agreed as follows:

"That the charges had been proved against the said Peter Heywood, James Morrison, Thomas Ellison, Thomas Burkitt, John Millward, and William Muspratt; and did adjudge them, and each of them, to suffer death,

by being hanged by the neck, on board such of his Majesty's ship or ships of war, and at such time or times, and at such place or places, as the commissioners for executing the office of Lord High Admiral of Great Britain and Ireland, etc, or any three of them, for the time being, should, in writing, under their hands, direct; but the Court, in consideration of various circumstances, did humbly and most earnestly recommend the said Peter Heywood and James Morrison to his Majesty's mercy; and the Court further agreed, that the charges had not been proved against the said Charles Norman, Joseph Coleman, Thomas M'Intosh, and Michael Byrne, and did adjudge them, and each of them, to be acquitted."

The Court was then opened and audience admitted, and sentence passed accordingly.

CHAPTER TEN

The King's Pardon – for Some

It was a very common feeling that Heywood and Morrison, the former in particular, had been hardly dealt with by the Court in passing upon them a sentence of death, tempered as it was with the recommendation to the king's mercy. It should, however, be remembered that the Court had no power to pass any other sentence but that, or a full acquittal. But however earnestly the Court was disposed towards the latter alternative, it could not, consistently with the rules and feelings of the service, have acquitted them. It is not enough in cases of mutiny (and this case was aggravated by the piratical seizure of a king's ship) that the officers and men in his Majesty's naval service should not take an active part. To be neutral or passive is considered to be the same as aiding and abetting. Besides, their remaining in the ship along with the mutineers, without having recourse to whatever means were available of leaving her, presumes a voluntary adherence to the criminal party.

The only fault of Heywood, and a pardonable one on account of his youth and inexperience, was his not ask-

ing Christian to be allowed to go with his captain – his not *trying* to go in time. M'Intosh, Norman, Byrne and Coleman were acquitted because they expressed a strong desire to go but were forced to remain. This was not only clearly proved, but they were in possession of written testimonies from Bligh to that effect; and so would Heywood have had, but for some prejudice that Bligh had taken against him in the course of the boat voyage home, for it is clear that Bligh knew he had been confined to his berth below.

In favour of three of the four men condemned without a recommendation, there were no mitigating circumstances. Millward, Burkitt and Ellison were armed in the mutiny from first to last; and Ellison not only left the helm to take up arms but, rushing aft towards Bligh, called out: "D—n him, I'll be sentry over him." The fourth man, Muspratt, was condemned only on the evidence of Lieutenant Hayward. This appears to have been duly appreciated by the Lords Commissioners of the Admiralty, and in consequence the poor man was reprieved and escaped a shameful death.

The family of young Heywood in the Isle of Man had been buoyed up, from various quarters, with the almost certainty of his full acquittal. From the 12th September, when the court martial first sat, till the 24th of that month, they were prevented, by the strong winds that cut off all

communication with England, from receiving any news whatever. But while Mrs Heywood and her daughters were imagining that everything would be most happily concluded, one evening a little boy, the son of one of their particular friends, ran into the room and told them, in the most abrupt manner, that the trial was over and all the prisoners condemned, but that Peter Heywood was recommended to mercy. He added that a man whose name he mentioned had told him this. The man was sent for and questioned, and he replied that he had seen it in a newspaper at Liverpool, from where he had just arrived in a small fishing boat, but had forgotten to bring the newspaper with him. The wretched family remained in this state of doubtful uncertainty for another whole week, harassed by the most cruel agony of mind, which no language can express.

The suspense into which the family in the Isle of Man had been thrown, by the delay of the mail boat, was painfully relieved on its arrival on the night of the 29th September, with the following letter from Mr Graham (Peter Heywood's adviser in the court martial):

"I have attended and given my assistance at Mr Heywood's trial, which was finished and the sentence passed about half an hour ago. Before I tell you what that sentence is, I must inform you that his life is safe, notwithstanding it is at present at the mercy of the king,

to which he is in the strongest terms recommended by the Court. That any unnecessary fears may not be productive of misery to the family, I must add, that the king's attorney general (who with Judge Ashurst attended the trial) desired me to make myself perfectly easy, for that my friend was as safe as if he had not been condemned."

Heywood had remained remarkably calm throughout his ordeal, especially since he knew that Bligh had deliberately and falsely blackened his character. Indeed, so perfectly calm was this young man under his dreadful calamity that, in a very few days after condemnation, his brother says, "While I write this, Peter is sitting by me making an Otaheitan vocabulary, and so happy and intent upon it, that I have scarcely an opportunity of saying a word to him; he is in excellent spirits, and I am convinced they are better and better every day. This vocabulary (dictionary) is a very extraordinary performance; it consists of one hundred full-written folio pages, the words alphabetically arranged, and all the syllables accented."

There is a note in Marshall's *Naval Biography* which shows one motive on Christian's part for keeping Heywood and Stewart in the ship. It is as follows: "Mr Stewart was no sooner released than he demanded of Christian the reason for his detention; upon which the latter denied having given any directions to that effect; and his assertion

was corroborated by Churchill, who declared that he had kept both him and Mr Heywood below, knowing it was their intention to go away with Bligh. 'In which case,' added he, 'what would become of us, if anything should happen to you; who is there but yourself and them to depend upon in navigating the ship?'"

It may be suspected, however, that neither Christian nor Churchill was telling the exact truth, and that Mr Heywood's case is, in fact, much stronger than he ever could have imagined. If Bligh had not acted the part of a prejudiced and unfair man towards him, he would have been acquitted by the Court on the same ground that Coleman, Norman, M'Intosh and Byrne were – namely, that they were detained in the ship against their will, as stated by Bligh in the narrative on which they were tried and also in his printed report.

It has been observed before that many things are set down in Bligh's original manuscript journal that have not appeared in any published document, and on this part of the subject there is, in the former, the following very important admission. "As for the officers, whose cabins were in the cockpit, there was no relief for them; *they endeavoured to come to my assistance, but were not allowed to put their heads above the hatchway.*" To say, therefore, that in the suppression of this passage Bligh acted with prejudice and unfairness is to make use of mild terms. It has

more the appearance of a deliberate act of malice, by which two innocent men might have been condemned to suffer a shameful death. One of them was actually brought into this predicament – the other only escaped it by a premature death in the wreck of the *Pandora.*

Churchill was quite right as to the motive for keeping these young officers, but Christian had, no doubt, another and a stronger motive – he knew how necessary it was to erect a sort of barrier between himself and his mutinous gang; he was too good an adept not to know that seamen will always pay a more ready and cheerful obedience to officers who are *gentlemen* than to those who may have risen to command from among themselves. It is, indeed, a common observation in the service that officers who have risen from *before the mast* are generally the greatest tyrants.

On the 24th October, the king's warrant was dispatched from the Admiralty, granting a full and free pardon to Heywood and Morrison, and a respite for Muspratt, which was followed by a pardon. The warrant also gave orders for carrying the sentence of Ellison, Burkitt and Millward into execution, which was done on the 29th, on board his Majesty's ship *Brunswick*, in Portsmouth harbour. On this melancholy occasion, Captain Hamond reports that "the criminals behaved with great penitence and decorum, acknowledged the justice of their sentence

for the crime of which they had been found guilty, and exhorted their fellow sailors to take warning by their untimely fate, and whatever might be their hardships, never to forget their obedience to their officers, as a duty they owed to their king and country." The captain adds, "A party from each ship in the harbour, and at Spithead, attended the execution, and from the reports I have received, the example seems to have made a great impression upon the minds of all the ships' companies present."

The same warrant that carried with it sadness to the friends of these unfortunate men was the bringer of joy to the family and friends of young Heywood. His sister, who had made great exertions to help obtain his freedom, wrote to her mother as follows:

"*Great Russell Street, Monday Morning, 29th October, half-past ten o'clock – the brightest moment of my existence!*

"My dearest Mamma, I have seen him, clasped him to my bosom, and my felicity is beyond expression! In person he is almost even now as I could wish; in mind you know him an angel. I can write no more, but to tell you, that the three happiest beings at this moment on earth, are your most dutiful and affectionate children,

"Nessy Heywood, Peter Heywood, James Heywood.

"Love to and from all ten thousand times."

The worthy Mr Graham adds, "If, my dearest Madam,

it were ever given for mortals to be supremely blest on earth, mine to be sure must be the happy family. Heavens! with what unbounded extravagance have we been forming our wishes! and yet how far beyond our most unbounded wishes we are blest! Nessy, Maria, Peter, and James, I see, have all been endeavouring to express their feelings. I will not fail in any such attempt, for I will not attempt anything beyond an assurance that the scene I have been witness of, and in which I am happily so great a sharer, beggars all description. Permit me however to offer my most sincere congratulations upon the joyful occasion."

And well did Heywood's future conduct fulfil that promise. Notwithstanding the unlucky manner in which the first five years of his service in the navy had been passed, two of which were spent among mutineers and far from home, and eighteen months as a close prisoner in irons, in which condition he was shipwrecked and within an ace of drowning – he re-entered the naval service under the auspices of his uncle, Commodore Pasley, and of Lord Hood, who had presided at his trial. These officers earnestly recommended him to embark again as a midshipman without delay, Lord Hood offering to take him into the *Victory*, under his own immediate patronage. In the course of his service, to qualify for the commission of lieutenant, he was under the respective commands of

three or four distinguished officers who had sat on his trial, from all of whom he received the most flattering reports of praise and approval.

It is not here intended to follow Mr Heywood through his honourable career of service during the long and arduous contest with France and in the several commands with which he was entrusted. In a note of his own writing, it is stated that, on leaving the *Montague*, in July 1816, he came on shore after having been actively employed at sea twenty-seven years, six months, one week and five days out of a service in the navy of twenty-nine years, seven months and one day. Having reached nearly the top of the list of captains, he died, leaving behind him a high and unblemished character in that service, of which he was a most honourable, intelligent and distinguished member.

CHAPTER ELEVEN

The Fate of the *Bounty* and the Mutineers

It was twenty years after the mutiny that news first came to Britain of what had happened to Fletcher Christian, the remaining mutineers and the ship. An American vessel, the *Topaz*, made a landing on the Pacific island of Pitcairn and discovered a small but flourishing community, under the charge of one Alexander Smith, who turned out to be the same person as John Adams, once a member of the *Bounty*'s crew. The island was well ruled and inhabited by handsome and cheerful young people, descendants of the *Bounty*'s men and of the Tahitian women who had accompanied them. Smith willingly told the visitors how the island had been colonised. This out-of-the-way and inaccessible isle had been deliberately picked by Christian. Finding no good anchorage close to the island, and the *Bounty* being too weakly manned again to entrust themselves in her at sea, Christian determined to run her aground, into a small creek against the cliff. This was in order to make it easier to get out of

her such articles as might be of use, or necessary, for establishing a settlement on the island and to land the pigs, goats and poultry that they had brought from Otaheite. Having accomplished this point, he ordered the *Bounty* to be set on fire, with the view, probably, of preventing any escape from the island and also to remove an object that, if seen, might excite the curiosity of some passing vessel and thus be the means of revealing his hiding place.

His plan succeeded, and, by Adams's account, everything went on smoothly for a short time, but it was clear enough that this misguided and ill-fated young man was never happy after the rash and criminal step he had taken. He was always sullen and morose, and committed so many acts of wanton oppression that he very soon incurred the hatred and detestation of his companions in crime. It seems, indeed, that he practised that same overbearing conduct over them of which he had accused his commander, Bligh. The object he had in view when he last left Otaheite had now been accomplished – he had discovered an uninhabited island away from the common route of ships and had established himself and his associates. So far, there was a chance that he had escaped all pursuit, but there was no escaping from his own nature. The fate of this misguided young man, brought on by his ill-treatment both of his associates and the Otaheitans he had carried off with him, was such as

might be expected – he was shot by an Otaheitan while digging in his field, about eleven months after they had settled on the island. His death was only the start of feuds and killings, which ended in the total destruction of the whole party, except Adams and Young.

By Adams's account, the settlers from this time became divided into two parties, and their grievances and quarrels proceeded to such a height, that each took every opportunity of putting the other to death. Old John Adams was himself shot through the neck, but the ball entered the fleshy part only, and he was able to make his escape and avoid the fury of his assailants. The immediate cause of Christian's murder was his having forcibly seized the wife of one of the Otaheitan men, which so angered the rest that they not only sought his life but those of others who might, they thought, be disposed to pursue the same course.

Christian was a gentleman by birth and an officer in his Majesty's service, and was always so addressed. But why was he murdered within two years (one account says only nine months) after the party reached the island? The reason was his inability to lead the community and his oppression of the Otaheitans. That Christian was always uneasy in his mind about his own safety is proved by his having selected a cave at the very top of the high ridge of craggy hills that runs across the island as his

intended place of refuge. In the event of any ship of war discovering the hiding place of the mutineers, he was resolved to retreat to this cave and to sell his life as dearly as he could. In this recess he always kept a store of provisions, and near it he built a small hut, well concealed by trees, which served the purpose of a watchhouse. "So difficult," says one visitor to the scene "was the approach to this cave, that even if a party were successful in crossing the ridge, he might have bid defiance, as long as his ammunition lasted, to any force."

The reflection of his having sent adrift to die on the wide ocean (for no other outcome was likely), no fewer than nineteen people, all of whom, one only excepted, were innocent of any offence towards him, must have constantly haunted his mind and left him little disposed to be happy and cheerful.

CHAPTER TWELVE
Conclusion

Many useful and salutary lessons of conduct may be drawn from this eventful history, more especially by officers of the navy, both old and young, as well as by those subordinate to them. In the first place, it most strongly points out the dreadful consequences that are almost certain to ensue from a state of insubordination and mutiny on board a ship of war; and the equally certain fate that, at one time or other, awaits all those who have the misfortune to be concerned in a transaction of this revolting nature. In the present instance, the dreadful retribution which overtook them, and which was evinced in a most extraordinary manner, affords an awful and instructive lesson to seamen. From it they may learn, that although the guilty may be secured for a time in evading the punishment due to the offended laws of society, yet they must not hope to escape the pursuit of Divine vengeance.

It will be recollected that the number of persons who remained in the *Bounty*, after her piratical seizure, and who were charged with the crime of mutiny, was twenty-

five; that these subsequently separated into two parties, sixteen having landed at Otaheite, and afterwards taken from thence in the *Pandora*, as prisoners, and nine having gone with the *Bounty* to Pitcairn's Island.

Of the sixteen taken in the *Pandora*:–

1 Mr Peter Heywood, midshipman, sentenced to death, but pardoned, and later became a distinguished captain in the Royal Navy.
2 James Morrison, boatswain's mate, sentenced to death, but pardoned.
3 William Muspratt, commander's steward, sentenced to death, but pardoned.
4 Thomas Burkitt, seaman, condemned and executed.
5 John Millward, seaman, condemned and executed.
6 Thomas Ellison, seaman, condemned and executed.
7 Joseph Coleman, armourer, tried and acquitted.
8 Charles Norman, carpenter's mate, tried and acquitted.
9 Thomas M'Intosh, carpenter's crew, tried and acquitted.
10 Michael Byrne, seaman, tried and acquitted.
11 Mr George Stewart, midshipman, drowned in HMS *Pandora*.
12 John Sumner, seaman, drowned in HMS *Pandora*.
13 Richard Skinner, seaman, drowned in HMS *Pandora*.
14 Henry Hillbrant, cooper, drowned in HMS *Pandora*.

15 Charles Churchill, master-at-arms, murdered by Matthew Thompson.
16 Matthew Thompson, seaman, murdered by Churchill's friends in Otaheite.

Of the nine who landed on Pitcairn's Island:–

1 Mr Fletcher Christian, acting lieutenant, murdered.
2 John Williams, seaman, murdered.
3 Isaac Martin, murdered.
4 John Mills, gunner's mate, murdered.
5 William Brown, botanist's assistant, murdered.
6 Matthew Quintal, seaman, put to death by Young and Adams in self-defence.
7 William M'Koy, seaman, became insane, and killed by throwing himself from a rock.
8 Mr Edward Young, midshipman, died of asthma.
9 Alexander Smith, *alias* John Adams, seaman, died a natural death in 1829.

Glossary

aft at, near or towards the stern of a ship.
aftermost closest to the stern of a vessel.
afterpart the part towards the stern of a ship.
astern behind a ship; at or towards the rear of a ship.
a-weather on the weather side of a ship, i.e. towards the wind.
barrico (*pl* **barricoes**) a small cask or barrel.
before the mast the sailors' quarters in the bow of a vessel.
boatswain a ship's officer in charge of sails, rigging, etc.
booby (*pl* **boobies**) a tropical sea bird with a straight stout bill and white plumage with darker markings.
boom a spar on which a sail is stretched.
breadfruit a tree of the Pacific Islands that bears a fruit that, when baked or roasted, has a texture like that of bread.
condign serene.
cordage a quantity of cords or ropes; ropes and rigging.
cutter a light boat carried by a ship, fitted for rowing or sailing.